WIIGWAASKINGAA

"Land of Birch Trees"

Ojibwe Stories
By
Arthur J. McGregor

"Nmenhs" - Little Sturgeon

Editor: Julie Wilder

Ojibwe Editor: Mary E. Wemigwans

Copyright @1999 by Julie Wilder c/o Blue Moon Publishing, 99.
Whitefish River First Nation
Birch Island, Ontario, P0P 1A0

Editor: Julie Wilder
Ojibwe Editor: Mary E. Wewmigwans
Illustrations: Jake Wilder
Typesetting and Design: Finian Paibomesai Design & Illustration
First Edition: 2000
Second Edition: 2005
Front cover: Design: Finian Paibomesai - Photo: Arthur McGregor
Back cover: Feature: Whitefish River First Nation Artist: Finian Paibomesai
                Feature: Wikwemikong First Nation
                        Ojibwe Language Editor: Mary E. Wemigwans
                Feature: Whitefish River First Nation Editor: Julie Wilder
Printed and bound in Canada by Anishinabe Printing, Maniwaki, Quebec
Canadian Cataloguing in Publication Data
McGregor, Arthur J. (Arthur Joseph), 1917-
Wiigwaaskingaa, "Land of Birch Trees"
Text in English and Ojibway.
Includes bibliographical references and index.
ISBN 0-9685103-0-2

    1. Ojibwa Indians--Folklore.   2. Ojibwa Indians--Ontario--Birch Island--Folklore. 3. Ojibwa Indians--History. 4. Ojibwa Indians--Ontario--Birch Island--History. 5. Ojibwa Language--Readers. I. Wilder, Julie. II. Title.
E99.C6M34 1999   398.2'0899730713   C99-910599-X

Acknowledgments

Extending my sincerest appreciation to Roy Piepenburg Sr. and Earth Harmony Publishing for their advice and knowledge that assisted me in this endeavour.

The persons responsible for the most important developments of this Book are: Art and Violet McGregor, Mary E. Wemigwans, Finian Paibomesai, Jake Wilder, Corrina Wilder, Richard Shawanda, and Daniel Wildcat.

My sincerest appreciation to George McGregor, Murray McGregor, Violet McGregor and Veronica Kelly (McGregor), Mary Jane Charette and Duncan McGregor for their assistance with the Ojibwe Language Editor Mary E. Wemigwans

We gratefully acknowledge the support from the people of Wiigwaaskingaa, Mr. George Gardner of Lafarge Canada, McGregor Bay Association, and Ojibwe Cultural Foundation.

The McGregor Bay Association
McGregor Bay Ontario

Ojibwe Cultural Foundation

Special Note from the Editor

"Time Immemorial", a term often used by our Aboriginal peoples most eloquent speakers, which refers to our Aboriginal peoples essence of existence, "as long as the grass grows, the waters flow and the sun shines". So too, Time Immemorial, refers to our Aboriginal Elders; through their Oral Traditions (storytelling), the tales, myths, legends, anecdotes and the subtle lessons or morals derived from these stories.

Our Elders, like fine wine - aged to perfection, with a robust, hearty flavour and bittersweet taste, to be savoured and enjoyed. So too, are our Elders, aged to perfection, with a robust, hearty flavour of knowledge and spirit, as well as, a bittersweet taste of wisdom, to be enjoyed and savoured. All, that our Aboriginal peoples learn about ourselves and our Heritage are the greatest gifts that our Elders possess. Through Oral Tradition, it is the Elders that pass on to our young Aboriginal peoples this knowledge and wisdom, as it has been for Time Immemorial. Our Elders, the most valuable resource persons a Community can have, to be respected, these keepers of knowledge and wisdom, whom are also, the strength of a community. So too, with the passage of time we lose our Elders and the knowledge they possess.

With the approach of a new Millennium, it is important that we document the knowledge that our Elders possess. It is these people whom have witnessed the greatest technological changes that have occurred in their lifetime, and yet, can still recall Aboriginal life before these changes have occurred. The younger generation of Aboriginal peoples are in danger of losing their Culture, Language, and the subtle lessons of life, which are provided through Oral Tradition (storytelling) of the myths, legends, and anecdotes in which our Elders possess.

One Community, has an Elder, whose greatest concern is the rate at which the Aboriginal peoples are losing their Culture and Language. With this concern in mind, the focus is on the valuable contributions that this Elder has made, and as well, as it should be for other Elders in each and every community.

Miigwech,

Table of Contents

Biography

In the year 1917, on the 25th day of September, Joseph Arthur McGregor was born, at the Old Village of Birch Island to William and Julia McGregor (nee Recollet). Their son Joseph Arthur McGregor was also named "Nmenhs" which in Ojibwe, means "little Sturgeon". His Father, William McGregor was Chief of the Whitefish River Indian Band for 26 years(1921-32, 1939-54). Art, the eldest of three brothers, George and Murray; also had eight sisters: Agnes, Florence, Genevieve, Barbara, Susan, Mary Louise, Marion and Veronica and they all lived at the Old village for awhile, then the family moved to the new village, where Birch Island is currently, located.

In his early years, Art was fortunate, he never went to Residential School, but had attended Grade School, Senior Class Grade Four. He stopped his education for a short while, when his father (William) had taken ill. He supported and helped his mother Julia, with the family, tending livestock, gardening, making Maple syrup, during his fathers illness. The Indian Agent suggested to his father to remove Art from school completely, but William did not like the Indian Agents suggestion, so Art was enrolled in Cadet School (Day School), so he could continue to help his mother with the family and attend school, also.

In 1935, Art had enrolled in Correspondence courses offered by the Guelph Agricultural College. It had taken three years to complete, and Art received a Diploma in Agriculture and Animal Farming, from the college. Art studied further, Heavy Equipment at Sturgeon Falls for three years and upon completion worked for Allens Construction building Highway 17.

In 1952, at the age of 35 years, he married Violet Wemigwans. They made their home in Birch Island, and shortly thereafter, their first daughter was born, Marie; then a son, Tim; followed by daughters Julia and Susan. Then, in the early 60s Brian, a son was born; followed by daughters Inez, Bonnie, Marriette, and finally, a son, Robert born in the late 60s .

To support his ever growing family, Art grew vegetables, maintained a small farm, with a few pigs, chickens, horses and a goat. He involved all of the family in gardening and tending animals. Besides gardening, Art worked outside the community to support his family, not traveling to far from home. He continued to work for awhile with Allens Construction.

In the early 1960s, Art worked awhile for Ontario Hydro, on the early wiring crew, which was providing power to the cottages in McGregor Bay and Killarney areas. Ontario Hydro had a boat called the "Nanabush" and several other scows which serviced the Bay areas. Art had also been offered employment with a Trucking Company, for the Vancouver run which would take him from home and his family, the run consisted of 8 days on the run and only 2 days off. He declined this offer out of concern for his family. There were no telephones or ambulance service for them, if an emergency arose.

At times, even he would take people to the hospital, since he was one of three persons, at that time, lucky enough to own an automobile. Some emergency trips to the hospital, people would wake him at 4 or 5 in the morning to drive them there. Other employment, such as Carpentry work, became more suitable, since it did not take him far from home. Carpentry work was local, in the McGregor Bay areas, for various cottagers and outfitters. Although this work was seasonal, every year he tended to planting and weeding his garden, as well as, involving the whole family in gardening.

In the Fall and Winter, he went hunting, fishing and did some trapping and cutting Pulp wood for his livelihood and he also, tended to the Sugar Camp, making of Maple Syrup in the Spring.

In 1984, Art retired, but still remained active, and still continuing to work doing little carpentry jobs here and there in the McGregor Bay areas. Shortly, after retirement, Art and his wife Violet, began to make and sell Crafts, travelling to various Pow-Wows and other events, during the Spring, Summer and Fall. Every year during the Pow-Wow season they would travel to these events and have established a Trade Route where they would meet new friends and greet old friends.

In the Fall of 1995, Art suffered a Stroke which left the right side of his body, paralyzed. He started a long regime of therapy to partially regain mobility in his right side. Today, he has partial dexterity in his right hand and is still very active, but requires a cane to walk, most times and still is as productive as ever. Gardening and making Maple Syrup, are still the most important activities of his life. Along with the crafts that He and his wife, Violet produce together, a successful Business venture, they travel the Pow-Wow trail. As they journey along to various Pow-Wows during the Spring, Summer and Fall, Art and Violet are sometimes accompanied by some of their Grandchildren, in all, they have 29 Grandchildren and 7 Great Grandchildren. Some of their Grandchildren are Pow-Wow dancers as well, and sometimes they dance with their Grandmother at these Pow-Wows.

As a respected Elder, "Gete-zhitwaawin" a keeper of the "old ways" and the oldest method of communicating, Art is often called upon too deliver Oral Traditions, in English and as well, in the Ojibwe Language. Both Art and his wife, Violet are very fluent Ojibwe speakers. In 1997, Art was involved in translating Ojibwe Language tapes, which were recorded in the early 1930s. These tapes were recordings of his Grandfather Gregor McGregor in which he spoke in the Ojibwe Language. These translations from Ojibwe to English were done for Professor J. Nichols of the University of Manitoba.

Even though, life has been a little rough on Art, he still remains very much active in the community, as well as on the Pow-Wow trail. Art and Violet are very well renown Artisans, Respected Elders and Friends of many. They reside in Birch Island, but are often away from home, at Elders conferences, Meetings, and of course, Pow-wows.

Introduction

For 82 years, Art McGregor has lived on the Whitefish River First Nation at Birch Island. As an Elder of this community, Oral Tradition or storytelling has been an important part of his life.

Oral Tradition is a key in understanding ourselves as Ojibwe people. Recollections of stories and reflections, the good and the bad are essential in understanding our History, Language and Culture.

Oral Tradition provides subtle lessons in spiritual beliefs, traditions, protocol, laws and morals which are essential tools in learning about ourselves, and serve to guide us in our endeavours. As Penny Petrone describes in *Native Literature in Canada, From the Oral Tradition to Present*, "communicating the respective histories and rules of belief and behaviour of the diverse tribes, and perpetuating their specific world views that gave the cosmos its origin, order and meaning. It bound "the sacred and the profane, the individual and the tribal, the past and the present and future, and it encompasse{d} the teller, the listener, the tribe, and the land, and the universe. By transmitting specific cultural knowledge with its specific meanings and messages, it helped strengthen tribal identity and provide continuity." (1990 p.3-4)

Just as important as the preservation of Oral Tradition, is preservation of the Language, which also provides identity and is essential in learning about ourselves and for the future generations of Ojibwe people of Wiigwaasskingaa (Birch Island).

The Language that our Grandfathers and Grandmothers had once used are near extinction. As Basil H. Johnston explains in the article *"One Generation from Extinction"* an excerpt from *"Native Writer and Canadian Writing"* which he states "They all spoke their tribal language, Anishninawbe, (Ojibwe) . When these elders passed away, so did a portion of the tribal language come to an end as a tree disintegrates by degrees and in stages until it is no more; and though infants were born to replenish the loss of life, not any one of them will learn the language of their Grandfathers or Grandmothers to keep it alive and to pass on to their descendants. Thus Language dies."(1990 pg.10)

These two keys: Oral Tradition and Language are essential to unlocking the essence of our beings as Ojibwe people. Moreover, Oral Tradition provides identity and prosperity for our future, just as does the Language. The preservation of Oral Tradition and Language are equally important for the People of Wiigwaaskingaa (Birch Island).

In this compilation of Oral Tradition (Storytelling), Art provides two stories; one of which refers to "Enjibwaajigeng" or Dreamers Rock that depicts Ojibwe Cultural information and reflects on the Spirituality of our peoples. In this Oral Tradition provided by Art, this story appears first and foremost, because in all that we do, we pray for guidance, wisdom, and strength to begin and end our days.

The other story, "Sinmedweek" or Bell Rock, of which Art provides is an Oral Tradition account, this story provides people with the origins of the People of Wiigwaaskingaa. This story can be traced back to the Historical era known as the "Fur Trade", and also provides information on the events leading up to the evolvement of the people of Birch Island or "Wiigwaaskingaa". Both these stories constitute the origins of the people of Wiigwaaskingaa, through the History, Culture and Language provided by Oral Tradition.

Art also, gives other stories of Oral Tradition in which also contributes to the essence of our being. He speaks of Bgojinishnaabenhsag, the little people; and Akinini, the earth man; and Pahiinsag, the river dwellers. These stories are based in the realm of Aboriginal peoples, although there are many different names and versions, of these beings in other tribes.

Long ago, the Ojibwe people were very religious, in their own beliefs, values and traditions. There were powers that could be described as natural and unnatural powers, which were derived from Mother Earth, our Creator. In order to understand the stories contained within, there must be some degree of belief. For some of us, occurrences within the universe can be natural and thus, explained; for other occurrences, the unexplained must be plainly accepted. For example, the belief in a higher power, although not tangible, there is belief. This is the case with these stories, which remain uniquely and traditionally, ours.

As Penny Petrone states in **Native Literature in Canada, From Oral Tradition to Present**, in reference to Oral Tradition, "Essentially religious in character it contains the spiritual beliefs, traditions, laws, morals and history of the culture-group transmitted by the elders of the tribe in order to explain the mysteries of the universe."(1990 p.11) "Early non-native readers, therefore, with their different conceptions of time, space, material possessions, phenomena of nature, the super-natural, and their different sense of humour and language - regarded Indian narra-tives as quaint and childish fairy tales, as superstition or primitive folklore."(Ibid.) However viewed by non-natives, Bgojinishnaabensag, the little people; Pahiinsag, the river dwellers; and Akinini, the earthman provides a sense of identity and sub-tle lessons that are combined with a little humor.

For the people of Wiigwaaskingaa, these stories are still very much a part of our identity as Ojibwe people, these stories that Art provides are based on actual accounts. Art offers these stories in the Ojibwe Language. This compilation of Oral Traditions are very important aspect of the preservation of our History, Culture and Language.

Beginning with the Historical perspective of the 1500's to 1790, the focus will be on the events of the Fur Trade and the early canoe routes used by these Traders and the Ojibwe people. Then, the perspective will narrow to reveal the Historical events at the La Cloche Islands and La Cloche channel, which will provide their origins.

A further facet of History, the early 1800's to 1940's will provide accounts of the evolvement of the village, Wiigwaaskingaa. The purpose of employing Historical information is to identify the Ojibwe people of Wiigwaaskingaa and to collaborate historical details of the evolvement of the village known as Wiigwaaskingaa.

The Historical Perspective 1500 - 1790

In the early 1500s European fisherman in the St. Lawrence River area had dis-covered another source of wealth, the Beaver pelt. Soon, there began a boom for the Beaver pelt, Europe was in demand for this precious commodity. By the

1600's, the Fur Trade had escalated into rivalries between the French and the English for the control of the wealth of the Fur Trade and as well, this new land. With the Beaver pelts in near extinction in the St. Lawrence and east areas, the Hurons became middlemen, bringing furs from the Indians of the interior, to be traded directly to the Trading Companies.

As Patterson explains in *The Canadian Indian, A History since 1500*, "The most significant tribe of middlemen... were the Hurons. They were a people well suited of trading and had a tradition of having been traders prior to the coming of the European..." (p. 66) Further, that the village of "Huronia was geographically suited for an important trading position. It was located on the shore of Georgian bay along established canoe routes...(p.67) So, prior to the arrival of the Europeans, there existed an economic structure in which the Aboriginal peoples actively participated. "The French observed this trading relation in 1615..."(ibid.) and Samuel de Champlain, a cartographer and explorer for the French began the inland campaign for the control of the Fur Trade. And as well, began to employ the established trading system and routes, which was established by the Aboriginal people. As Gutsche explains in *The North Channel and St. Marys River, A Guide to History*, he "arrived at Georgian Bay and established a trading alliance with the Huron and Odawa." (1997 p. xvi)

Soon to follow were the English, thus, began the ruthless pursuit of the control of the monopoly of the Fur Trade and the lands of the Great Lakes region. "The French allied the Hurons and the British allied the Iroquois" (Ibid.) for the control of the Upper Great Lakes. This became a fierce competition, the Iroquois went to war against the Huron nation, and with the successful eradication of the Huron nation, the Iroquois and the British counterparts began their campaign for the control of the Great Lakes monopoly. With the Huron eliminated, as Gutsche explains in *The North Channel and The St. Marys River, A Guide to History*, "the Iroquois shifted their attention to the Ojibwe and the Odawa" (1997. p xviii.) and the Great Lakes region.

With this inland campaign into the Great Lakes region, the French and the English employed the use of an "ancient canoe route" as Greenman explains in *Old Birch Island Cemetery And The Early Historic Trade Route* (1951, p.1) to the interior via the waterways "from Montreal up to the Ottawa River to Lake Nipissing via Mattawa River, from Lake Nipissing to Georgian Bay by way of the French River thence to Killarney" (Ibid. p. 3) through Cloche Channel "and west to the North Channel" (Ibid) to St.Mary's River with connections to "Sault Ste. Marie or St. Ignace" (Ibid)

This early historic trade route was used by the Hudson Bay Company, the first Trading Company in operation in 1670 and latter by the Northwest Company in 1783. The fierce competition between these two companies and other Companies, as Gutsche explains in *The North Channel and St. Marys River, A Guide To History*, such as the "Southwest Company based out of Mackinac Island, as well as a number of smaller trading groups. Rival companies entered into a "no holds barred" competition". (1997 p. xxi) Trading furs for European goods such as kettles, axes, tools, beads etc. were being replaced by Liquor. As well, Gutsche explains "Liquor became the currency of choice"(1997 p. xxii) The Fur Trade had escalated into a ruthless mayhem with devastating effects for the Huron and soon, the Ojibwe peoples.

By the late 1700s, with the Fur Trade, pitting men against men, nation against nation for the control of the Interior. With the addition of Liquor, being an ingredient to create catastrophe, the Hudson Bay Company, the Northwest Company, and a succession of other small Trading Companies set their sights on establishing Trading Posts in the vicinity of the La Cloche Channel and La Cloche Island. As Pitawankwat explains in *The History of Birch Island*, among these Fur Trading Companies, was a Fur Trader, "Scottish Captain Alexander McGregor . He settled on the point on the mainland southwesterly from Old Birch Island. Further, as J. D. Cameron, the factor at the Hudsons Bay Company post at Lacloche, states in his August 25, 1843 letter to Governor Simpson: "There is another opponent against us called McGregor. He has begun a house two years ago on the mainland opposite to Lacloche, which he had finished this summer." (1978)

In this letter, J. D. Cameron uses the word "opponent" in reference to McGregor, which indicates that, indeed, there was a competition for the Trading area, and that the presence of McGregor is not a welcomed one. So, with this recipe for catastrophe, this would be the pinnacle of events that would prove disastrous for the people at La Cloche or Bell Rocks.

La Cloche 1615-1790

Amidst this mayhem, and along this "ancient canoe route", was an area known as "La Cloche or Cloche" a French word meaning "Bell". As Morse explains in *Fur Trade Canoe Routes of Canada/Then and Now*, he states it is "so called from some of its rocks ringing like a bell on being struck." (1969 p. 66) This area comprises of the La Cloche Peninsula, La Cloche Mountains, the La Cloche Channel, the Great La Cloche Island and the Little La Cloche Island and La Cloche Lake. It was in this area, in 1761, that Alexander Henry, spoke of an Indian village situated "on an island called La Cloche, because there is a rock, standing on a plain, which, being struck, rings like a bell.

Also, Alexander Henry states in *Travels and Adventures*, "I found the Island inhabited by a large village of Indians, whose behaviour was at first full of civility and kindness". (Henry 1809 p. 34) In this statement, he refers to the character of the people he encountered. But, also reflects on the change in their character, upon learning his background.

Within the hostilities and the fierce competitions between rivaling trading companies, Alexander Henry is accosted, as he states "and we remained on friendly terms, till, discovering that I was an Englishman, they told my men, that the Indians at Michilimackinac, would not fail to kill me, and that therefore, they had a right to a share of the pillage. Upon this principle, as they said, they demanded a keg of rum, adding, that if not given to them, they would proceed to take it."(Ibid.)

This statement, by Henry in 1761, suggests the degree of mayhem and ruthlessness resulting from the Fur Trade, but also reflects on the good nature of the people at the village at Bell Rock.

Historically, the origins of the people living within that village, at that time may well have been, established to intercept the marauding Iroquois and their British allies. As Schmalz states in *The Ojibwe of Southern Ontario*, "It is likely that Champlain met some of the Ojibwe-speaking people as early as 1615 on the east shores of Georgian Bay. Because of the Iroquois attack from the southeast on the Huron and their Ojibwe allies, the Saulteaux, Nikikouek, Marameg, and Outchougai united for purposes of defence and over time, became the people called Ojibwe." (1991 p. 4-5)

Further, archaeological evidence suggests that the village at La Cloche may have been established long before the arrival of the Europeans. In, *Old Birch Island Cemetery And The Early Historic Trade Route*, Greenman refers to an early site located "about one quarter of a mile south of the ridge, on Great La Cloche Island. This area was evidently "the camping site", and that "the finding of small fragments of pottery and flakes of quartzite and flint" suggests that this site "indicates occupation in pre-contact times".(1951 p12-13) Given the evidence of this site , which suggests occupation in pre-contact times, it is likely that this ancient canoe route had been used by the Ojibwe peoples and others long before the arrival of the Europeans. As well, Oral Tradition tells of the Bell Rocks served as an early warning device, warning of impending attacks from waring nations of the South.

In addition, Greenman states, there was a grave site located on the ridge, which, "In the summer of 1938 two early historic sites were located. The first, on Great Cloche Island, was evidently the cemetery of the village mentioned by Henry...". The second site, contained archaeological evidence of pre-contact times, located one quarter mile south of the first site. In the first site, Greenman states that "Excavation of this cemetery had been carried on previously for many years, and nothing was left of the original graves..." and in addition, that at one time these graves had contained "European materials". (1951 p. 12)   This information suggests that this grave site located here, in which European items had been found, had once contained evidence of the Fur Trade era. In fact this site was an established village on the Fur Trade canoe route. As Oral Tradition reveals, there was a big village of people living at Bell Rock or Sinmedweek. They suffered a great tragedy, as a result of the furry of the Fur Trade. These people buried their dead, then moved away from there, altogether.

Significantly, during this time, there were external events, such as the War of 1812, the Treaty of Ghent, and other factors, that would consequently set the framework in the sequence of events for the Ojibwe people of Wiigwaaskingaa. A significant historical event as stated by Barry in *Georgian Bay* was "The Proclamation of 1763, which prohibited the taking of land from the Indians without their consent and approval of the British Crown." (p. 26) This event and another significant Historical events set the stage for eventual framework for the Ojibwe people of Wiigwaaskingaas permanent home.

"Wiigwaaskingaa M'nising" or Wardrope Island 1750 -1863

As History provides, the very first village of Birch Island was in the vicinity of La Cloche or Bell Rock, in which this information suggests that this village was established to intercept the marauding Iroquois there at the La cloche channel and the latter village, were settled by various bands of Indians in the Fur trade era. However, Oral Tradition tells of another tale, a tale of tragedy which resulted in the relocation of the Ojibwe people of Sinmedweek "Bell Rock".

After this tragedy, some of the people dispersed to Killarney, Sagamok, West Bay, Sheguiandah and all over, and other people moved to Wiigwaaskingaa Minising, or now, known as Wardrope Island. As Greenman states in *Old Birch Island Cemetery And The Early Historic Trade Route*, they settled on "the south end of this Island three quarters of a century or more ago." (1951 p.14), Greenman also states in reference to grave sites on Wardrope Island, "If the absence of native Indian pottery from Old Birch Island argues against a date before 1750, the presence of stone implements and cremation of the dead goes far to rule out anything after 1800." (p.16) This would suggest that, this area would have, more than likely, have had to have been settled between 1750 to 1800. In any case, Oral Tradition reveals that this was the next area of settlement for the Ojibwe people from La Cloche.

During this time, a lot of external events were taking place, the War of 1812, the Treaty of Ghent, to name a few and the dawning of a new era, in which Industry would play a vital role. As Gutsche explains in *The North Channel and The St. Marys River, A Guide To History*, "In the early 1830s, the North Channel and St. Marys region were still Indian territory, plied mainly by native and voyager canoes. This was about to change. The fur trade was on the wane and was being replaced by industries for which the Indians were no longer necessary. More and more schooners appeared, followed in the late 1830s by the steamships." (1997, p.xxviii)

With the onset of Industry, the people of Wiigwaaskingaa Minising would quickly adapt to these changes. Timber was replacing the Beaver pelt, as a commodity. In reference to these changes Greenman states in *Old Birch Island Cemetery And The Early Historic Trade Route*, "that this group of Indians man have cut timber at the north end of the Island for the steam-propelled boats that plied these waters in the nineteenth century, and then planted crops on the land thus cleared and dug pits for storage of produce from such plantings. This explanation is supported by the fact that there are no trees more than 10 inches in diameter in the area that occupied by the pits." (1951 p. 16) Although, this evidence suggests that the Wiigwaaskingaa people chose to settle here, other factors would reveal that in the advent of Industry, Wiigwaaskingaa Minising was a temporary settlement.

The next big boom in the area was Lumbering. Oral Tradition provides this insight, the big lumber companies moved in and the Ojibwe people were selling wood to these lumber companies, and these companies fuelled the schooners and later tug boats that burned wood to make them go, like steam engines. It was all Birch trees, here at one time, (referring to the Island) it was all white on that side of the Island, and big trees, too. The trees were the size of your outstretched arms, circled. Just like a mountain, when your paddling by, because the trees started from the shore and went straight back.

Oral Tradition also, reveals that the name of present day Wiiwaaskingaa, is derived from the village at Wiigwaaskingaa Minising and the people settled here on the south end of the Island. (Wardrope) As Greenman states "In any event the Indians of this Reserve formerly lived, by their own account, on the south end of Old Birch Island, and that is the origin of the name of their present Reserve. Statements as to the period of occupation of Old Birch Island are vague, but would seem to have been 75 or 100 years ago." (1951, p. 57) With the temporary settlement at Wiigwaaskingaa Minising being influenced by economic growth, there were Historical changes, as well, in which would provide the people of Wiigwaaskingaa, a more permanent home.

The most significant Historical event, as stated by Pitawanakwat in *The History of Birch Island*, "The Robinson Huron Treaty of 1850, is paramount for the permanent residency of the people of Birch Island. This Treaty, signed on September 09, 1850, at Sault Ste. Marie, which designated Reserves, for the Ojibwe people, covered a great expanse of land along the area known as the North shore, from Owen Sound to the southern tip of Lake Superior.

For the surrender of lands, a small number of reservations were set forth, and designated for the Ojibwe people. The chiefs and bands retained the same title as before the Treaty, as guaranteed by the Royal Proclamation in 1763. On the 25th of October, 1851, the reserve for the People at Wiigwaaskingaa, was surveyed and completed and the Reserve boundaries set, by the provincial land surveyor engaged by the Commissioner of Crown Lands.

The tract of land set aside for the people of Birch Island is stated as follows "a tract of land now occupied by them, and contained between two rivers, called Whitefish River, and Wanabitaseke, seven miles inland" (1978) this is as described in the Robinson - Huron Treaty of 1850. With this Historical event, and other significant economic changes, the people of Wiigwaaskingaa, then moved to another location.

"Old Birch Island" Mainland 1850-1909

The most notable change, was the signing of the Robinson-Huron Treaty, in which a number of Chiefs signed at Sault Ste. Marie (Bawaakting). Also, in 1850, Chief Shawanoswe, a Medicine Man, became the most notable Chief of the Whitefish River Reserve at Wiigwaaskingaa. He was to have powers that derived from "Enjibwaajigeng"- Dreamers Rock. It is said that this man had powers to heal the ill, and people would travel great distances for this purpose. He was instrumental in providing the people of Wiigwaaskingaa a more permanent settlement. The people as well, adapted to the economic changes and had become once again, economically oriented.

As Oral Tradition reveals, the Island, once abundant with Birch trees, had been cut down and there was no trees left, there. So, they moved. People got work cutting wood for those steam engines. They went from Wardrope Island to the mainland to cut wood. So rather than paddle across from Wardrope Island to the Old village site, they settled here, on the mainland.

As Greenman states in **Old Birch Island Cemetery And The Early Historic Trade Route**, in reference to the move, "Later, this group of Indians moved to the mainland directly west, where the foundations of log houses are still to be seen." (pg.14) He also states that, "But the ultimate removal to the mainland opposite the west side of the Island was to the nearest arable land." (Ibid.) Not only had the people engaged in economic activities in which Timber was a suitable commodity, these people planted gardens and also, tended the production of Maple syrup, in the Spring. Fishing and Hunting were also part of their lifestyle. These people became more sedentary and began farming.

As well Greenman also states in reference to the mainland village. "There is "less than one hundred" Indians living in Birch Island in 1895, but inquiry has not brought forth any further details."(1951, p. 58)   He also states "Eventually, they moved to the mainland directly opposite the west side of Old Birch island, and this land is today a part of the Reserve, with a few farms and Maple Sugar camps." (Ibid.)

With the onset of a new era, the People of Wiigwaaskingaa adapted to the new world. The mode of travel, was also changing, the canoes and schooners that had once plied through the waters were being replaced with faster and bigger boats, these propelled by steam. The Steam engine was the most significant change, it changed their lifestyle, with the introduction of the steam propelled boats and the steam engine used in locomotives. The Railroad, the most significant railway system to change the people of Wiigwaaskingaa's way of life was the Algoma Eastern Railroad. Equally consistent with these changes, was the relocation of the village in order to adapt to the economic advancements.

Wiigwaaskingaa, Birch Island Village 1906 - Present.

The next move was to the land nearest to the Railroad in which, construction had began around 1906. The village at Old Birch Island mainland was relocated, once again, the Ojibwe people of Wiigwaaskingaa Minising, moved. As Greenman explains in *Old Birch Island Cemetery And The Early Historic Trade Route*, "This village was also abandoned, and the descendants of the occupants now live at the head of the western arm of McGregor Bay, where a ridge of limestone about 100 feet high separates McGregor Bay and the North Channel. This is Birch Island Reserve." (1951 p. 14)

Oral Tradition reveals that there was a trail here called Oogaa Miikan or "Pickerel Trail", it is the tract of land joining the McGregor Bay and the Bay of Islands. The people would use this trail, to go to Whitefish Falls to fish for pickerel. No one owned it. They would travel from all over, Wikwemikong, Killarney, West Bay and Sucker Creek, to use this trail for a short cut to Whitefish Falls.

With the Introduction of the Railway, as Pitawankwat states in *The History of Birch Island*, "the Algoma Eastern Railway came through the reserve in 1911" (1978). The inhabitants of Old Birch Island relocated to this area, the tract of land between the McGregor Bay and Bay of Islands. As Oral Tradition reveals, in and around 1909, some people from the Old village had jobs cutting trees for railroad ties, for the new railroad, they cut Cedar trees. There were great stands of timber and the Cedar trees were big, so big, that you could make eight railroad ties out of one tree. The people were getting five cents each for those cut railroad ties. So, as they cleared away the land, the Ojibwe people of Wiigwaaskingaa built their village, here. The village moved, closer to the railroad line. People began making permanent wood homes, log houses, here.

As well, Greenman states in relation the the site "The village of the Reserve is at the narrowest part of Cloche Peninsula between the westward extending arm of McGregor Bay and the North Channel, at the railroad station known as Poncet. The east shore of Old Birch Island faces McGregor Bay proper, which is defined on the south by McGregor Point, the north line of Baie Fine."(Ibid. p.57) Oral

Tradition also reveals the McGregor Bay was once named "Mnidoo Wiikwed" meaning Monster Bay because this bay was inhabited by large snakes, which lived on the thick trees in and around the shoreline. Some places were thick with these snakes. This Bay was renamed McGregor's Bay because it was settled by the decedents of Captain Alexander McGregor, and then finally, named just McGregor Bay.

The Ojibwe people began to settle here, to live in accordance with provisions made in the Robinson-Huron Treaty of 1850, and within the Reserve Boundaries set forth in this Treaty. A special feature of the Robinson Huron Treaty, was that the Indians "denied all rights to sell, lease or otherwise dispose of any portion of their reservations without the consent of the Superintendent General of Indian Affairs" as Pitawanakwat states in *The History of Birch Island (1978)*.

There had been many changes in accordance with the size of the original Reserve, such as the gradual disbursement of the areas known as Whitefish Falls, Lawson Quarry, Willisville and Charlton Lake.This was the result of outside companies coming in, Lumbering, Timber and Mining operations. Nonetheless, the people continued to settle permanently. As Pitawankwat explains in *The History of Birch Island*, "Between 1900 and 1950 the Whitefish River (Birch Island) people had weathered: three separate applications for reserve land , as well as others, a Spanish influenza epidemic, severe winters, the tourist industry, the construction of a church, school, railway and highway, the Depression, several leases of band land and had made various requests to have investigated the gradual disappearance of Indian Lands."(1978) There was a lot of activities at the village of Birch Island. As Oral Tradition reveals, a small Catholic church had been built in 1913, which was a frame building. School started in the Catholic church at the top of the hill, it had one classroom and a building behind it. J.C. Ross was one of the first teachers.

In 1925-1927 LaCloche channel at Swift Current was ordered opened by the Government, closed since the railway was built, the railroad went over top of it. Road construction began near Whitefish Falls and at Haystack with a lot of blasting going on and bridge construction, some of the local men where hired to work on the road construction around here. The road opened in 1927, this road was used in the summer, it was a dirt road to Little Current. The most permanent structure and hallmark, was the stone church at the top of the hill, built in 1940, while the wood structure remained a school.

Fishing and Tourism, became another boom, for the people at Birch Island. Most significantly, in 1943, was the visit from Franklin Delano Roosevelt, the President of the United States. He came via the railway and spent some days fishing here in the McGregor Bay and the Bay of Islands. His train was stationed at Birch Island for one week. William McGregor was Chief of Whitefish River Indian Reserve, at that time. Jonas Shawanda, played the fiddle along with some other musicians, they entertained the President at Birch Island Lodge, which was owned by Mrs. Corke. That was a big affair, that time, as Oral Traditions states. Security was heavy, since this trip was made during the second World War. Some of the young men from this community participated in this war. Some men returned and some did not.

In the latter part of this century, the people of Wiigwaaskingaa strived to retain their Treaty Rights. They face issues in Health, mental and physical; Education; Self Government; Land Claims; Repatriation of Their Ancestors; Economic Development; Hunting and Fishing Rights; and Environmental concerns. They face these issues and new challenges with strength derived from their spirituality and guidance of the Creator.

Today, the people of Wiigwaaskingaa, descendants of the people at La Cloche and as well, as Greenman states in *Old Birch Island Cemetery And The Early Historic Trade Route*, "The residents of Birch Island Reserve call themselves Ojibwe, and the native language is the Ottawa-Ojibway variant of Central Algonquian." (1951, p. 58) The present day village was settled by families whose names consisted of: McGregor, Nahwegahbow, Pitawanakwat, Recollet, Shawanda, Buzwa, Migwanabe (Andrews), Kagesheongai, Jacko, Paibomsia, (Walker) Wahsquonaikezhik (Paul), and Toulouse, Kitchemokman, Pakosigan, Francis in which all share an unique history.

The Ojibwe people of Wiigwaaskingaa have a unique legacy, a strong community built on this legacy, which provides inspiration, guidance and wisdom, even today. Although much had been written about Enjibwaajigeng - Dreamers Rock and Sinmedweek - Bell Rocks, all of these stories provide an intrinsic perspective of Wiigwaaskingaa. These stories provide insight into Spirituality, History, Culture and Language.

Bay of Islands

To: Espanola

N

Wiigwaaskinga
Birch Island

Highway 6

La Cloche Peninsula

Wiigwaaskingaa
Old Birch Island

La Cloche
Channel

Wiiwaaskingaa Mnising
Wardrope Island

Swift Current

McGregor Bay

To:
Manitoulin Island
Little Current

Enjibwaajigeng
Dreamers Rock

Frazer Bay

Little Cloche
Island

Sinmedwe'ek
Bell Rocks

By: Richard Shawanda, 1999

Contemporary Map of Wiigwaaskingaa

Ojibwe Stories

1. **Dreamer's Rock**   **Enjibwaajigeng**

2. **Bell Rocks**   **Sinmedwe'ek**

3. **Little People**   **Bgojinishnaaben'sag**

4. **Earth Man**   **Akinini**

5. **River Dwellers**   **Pahiinsag**

Ojibwe Translations for the above stories were reviewed and edited by Mary E. Wemigawans

Mother Earth - Shkakmikwe

Enjibwaajigeng - Dreamer's Rock

1   A long time ago, the Ojibwe people were very respectful of All Things on this Earth. Special gifts, tobacco, cedar, sage and sweetgrass were used to honour the spirits of these things. These teachings came from our Creator, Gzhe-mnidoo and Mother Earth, Shkakmikwe. The Creator and Mother Earth gave these people a gift, a sacred place, it is called Enjibwaajigeng or Dreamers Rock. Enjibwaajigeng is a sacred centre. Ojibwe people prayed, meditated and had vision-quests here. This place is used to teach young people, to grow spiritually and to continue these teachings. This place, was thought to be the closest point nearest to our Creator, Gzhe-Mnidoo.("Debendjiged", He who owns all things.)

2   Enjibwaajigeng, is a tall, high rock, surrounded by water, almost like an island. You could get there by foot from the south side. This is where Sunshine Alley is, and they have pow wows over there. If you go in a southern direction, you will find a path. It goes around in a southern direction, that is what you follow. You will arrive on top, you could walk a long time to get to the top of Enjibwaajigeng - Dreamers Rock. On the very top of the Rock, there is a hollowed out spot in the shape of person sleeping, this spot is the place where people came to pray, meditate, and fast/dream.

3   People came to pray and give Thanks to the Creator, Gzhe- Mnidoo, for their wellbeing, abundance of food, good hunts and for all that was good. Others sought spiritual guidance in good times and in troubled times. They would often leave offerings (gifts) to the Creator, in Respect and Thanks for all that was received. These offerings would consist of tobacco, sweetgrass, cloth, beads, or whatever was dear to them, or whatever deemed appropriate. Of these ceremonies conducted on Enjibwaajigeng - Dreamers Rock, all were and still are very sacred and spiritual.

Enjibwaajigeng - Dreamer's Rock

1 Mewzha, Jibwek aapji gii-mndaadendaanaawaan kina gegoo eteg gidkamig. Gchitwaa mshkikiin, semaa, giizhik, mshkodewashk, miinwaa wiingashk gii-nakaaznaawaan wii-mndaadenmaawaad baagaakwag ninda mshkikiin. Ninda kinoohmaagewinan, nahiing gii-bi-njibaamgadoon Gzhe-Mnidoo miinwaa Shkakmikwe. Gzhe-Mnidoo miinwaa Shkakmikwe gii-miinaan Nishnaaben miingowewziwin gechitwaawendaagog. "Enjibwaajigeng" dash maampi zhinkaade. Gchitwaawendaagod wii go maa. Enjibwaajigeng Nishnaabeg gii-namhaawag, gii-naanaagdawendamoog, miinwaa gii-gzaabwag. Enjibwaajigeng Nishnaabeg dankaaznaawaa ezhkiniiigjig wii-kinoohmaajgaaswaad weweni ji-ni-mnobb-maadziwaad miinwaa ji-ni-kinoohmaagewaad gcwiinwaa. Gii-dnenjigaade dash "Enjibwaajigeng" temgag besho oodi Gzhe-Mnidoo yaad. (Debendjged, kina gegoo debendang.)

2 "Enjibwaajigeng", gchi sin ezhpaapkaag aawan. Gaataayhiing n'biish te. Gegaa go mnis aawan. Gdaa-dgoshin wiigo bmaseyin, nahiing nikeyaa zhaawnong. Mii maampii teg Sunshine Alley, mii maa e-nji-jiingtamwaad. Iishpin zhaawnong nikeyaa zhaayan, ka mkaan miikaanhs. Miikaanhs oodi namo, zhaawnong nikeyaa ni biimskomo. Miish wi ge naagdooyan. Mii go ji-ni-dgoshnan oodi ishpiming "Enjibwaajigeng". Noomok (gnwezh) go gdaa-gidaakiiyegaadewse ji-ni-dgosh-nan oodi gidaabik. Wiimbaabkaa dash maa gidaabkong, dbishkoo go naa ooya nebaad zhengshing mzinshin. Mii maampii bemaadzijig gaa-nji-namhaawaad, gaa-nji-naanaagdawendamowaad, miinwaa gaa-nji-mkadekewaad gaa-nji-bwaa-jgewaad. Gchitwaawendaagod wii go maa gaa-njibwaajegewaad waakaaganing. Noongo geyaabi nji-namhaam waakaaganing.

3 Bemaadzijig gii-bi-zhaawag wii-namhaawaad miinwaa wii-miigwech-wi'aawaad Debenjged, Gzhe-Mnidoo. Nji go naa, mnobemaadziwin miinwaa, niibna miijim yaamwaad, mno ndawenjgewaad miinwaa kina gegoo wenjishing yaamwaad. Aanind ge'e gii-ndawaambdaanaawaa wii-naadmaagoziwaad wii-mno-maajiishkaawaad manj go pii go. Gii-ngadmowaawaan ko miingowewziw-nan Debenjged, mndaadenmaawaad miinwaa miigwechwi'aawaad kina gegoo gaa-zhi-miingowewziwaad. Mii dash ninda gaa-bgidnigeng, semaa, wiingashk, gdaagiigin, mnidoominensag, maage gegoo aapji gaa-zaagtoowaad. Giin go waa-bgidnigeyan. Kina go gegoo gaa-nankiiwaad "Enjibwaajigeng" gii-gchitwaawen-daagod, miinwaa gaa-nakaazwaajin gii-gchitwaawendaagodoon, geyaabi go noon-go.

4   Another teaching, Waaseyaabendamowin, was for young men making the transitional journey from youth to adulthood. These young men would fast, four days and four nights, while on Enjibwaajigeng - Dreamers Rock. They would be left alone. They were instructed not to eat. They fast. They may drink a little water. They would bide their time, meditating, praying or whatever they were instructed to do, by the Elder or Medicine man.

5   They would follow instructions of fasting, praying, meditating, until the fourth day, at this time during their sleep, they would be presented with a dream-gift from the Creator. It was through the interpretation of the dream-gift, by the Medicine man or Elders, that they would know where their life paths would lead them. Sometimes, they would receive a name from the Creator through the dream-gift. After the Fasting ceremony atop Enjibwaajigeng - Dreamers Rock, there would be time for rejoicing, a feast was held with singing and dancing at Sinmedwe'ek - Bell Rocks.

6   A long time ago, there was a young man named Shawanoswe. He fasted (his quest) was upon Enjibwaajigeng - Dreamers Rock. He was given healing power, and he dreamt of what he was going to be. He was going to be a great Medicine man and Chief. That was his vision. He was taken away after his vision. The spirits came and took him to Neyaabkong. He was gone for two days. He was taken there to be taught more by them. The people found him at Neyaabkong. The Elders came to tell him about his vision. By then, he knew what kind of work he had to do, he was already told that. People knew right away he was the Chief. He didn't make decisions for the people, he would ask the Elders. All, would go to the Elders and the Elders would sit around a fire, then they would tell them (vision quest) what their dreams meant and what the are to be.

7   To this very day, Native people come to pray, meditate and of course, conduct ceremonies atop Enjibwaajigeng - Dreamers Rock. People would come from far and wide to this place. Of course, there are still some people who do not hold reverence to this place, and consequently, this place has been closed to the public, for lack of this reverence. To those of you, whom have respect and reverence for this and any other sacred place, Enjibwaajigeng - Dreamer's Rock is still very much open, to you.   Miigwech.

4   Waaseyaabendamowin ge bezhig kinoohmaagewin. Shkinweg, waa-ni-niniwjig gii-mkadekewag niiwgon miinwaa niiwodbik gidaabik "Enjibwaajigeng" biinash ji-bwaadmowaad waa-aawaad. Nshike gii-yaawag gidaabik. Mii gaa-nindwaa wii-bwaa-wiisniwaad, wii-mkadekewaad, daa-mnikwenaawaa dash wiigo bangii nbi-ish. Gii-naanaagdawendamoog miinwaa gii-namhaawag miinwaa go gegoo go gaa-zhi-bgosendmindwaa wii-zhichgewaad. Gechipiitzid maage Mshkikinini gaa-zhi-bgosendmaad. Mshkikinini maage Gechipiitzid gaa-naad wii-zhichgewaad.

5   Gii-zhichgewag gaa-zhi-wiindamoondawaa, gii-mkadekcwag, gii-namhaawag, gii-naanaagdawendamoog. Baamaa dash eko niwogiizhgag, epichi nbaawaad, mii-gii-bwaajgewaad. Gzhe-Mnidoo gii-miinaan bwaajgewin-miingowewziwin. Gechipiitzijig maage Mishkikinini dash maanda bwaajgewin gii-aankanootaanaawaa waa-zhi-bmaadziwaad naagdowaad wi miikanwaa gi gaa-bwaajgejig. Noswin ge, naangodnoong gii-bwaadaanaawaa Gechipiitzijig gaa-aankanootmowaad. Gaa-shkwaa-mkadekewaad dash "Enjibwaajigeng" mii gii-maawnjiding. Mnwendaagziwin gii-te. Gii-zhangem, gii-niimidim, gii-ngamwag oodi Sinmcdwe'ek teg.

6   Gchi mewzha, gii-yaa Nishnaabe Shawanoswe gii-zhinkaazo. Gii-mkadeke "Enjibwaajigeng". Gii-miinaa noojmowin gzhkihewziwin, miinwaa gii-bwaadaan waa-aawid. Gii-bwaadaan Gchi-Mshkikinini miinwaa Gimaa wii-aawid. Mii iw gaa-naamdang. Gii-maajiigaazo maaba gaa-shkwaa-bwaajiged. Mnidoon gii-maa-jiingoon oodi Neyaabkong. Niizhgon go gii-wnishin. Wii-kinoohmowaawaad gi mii-gaa-nji-maajiigaazod. Wiinwaa dash gonda bemaadzijig gii-naanaawaan oodi Neyaabkong. Gechipiitzijig dash gii-bi-aankanootmowaawaan wi gaa naamdang. Zhaashgo dash wii maaba gii-gkendang waa-nankiid, gii-wiindmawaa niinaa oodi Neyaabkong. Miigo gii-gkenmind Gimaa aawid. Gechipiitzinjin gii-zhaamaan gegoo wii-naakniged. Kina go gii-zhaamaawaan Gechipiitzinjin. Gechipiitzijig gii-giitaabwag shkodeng, Gii-wiindmawaawaan gaa-naambdamwaad gonda gaa-bwaajgejig miinwaa waa'aawaad.

7   Geyaabi go noongo, Nishnaabeg bi-zhaawag "Enjibwaajigeng" wii-bi-namhaawaad, wii-bi-naanaagdawendamowaad, wii-bi-gzaabwaad. Bemaadzijig ggwetaani waasa aanind gii-bi-njibaawag maa gaa-bi-zhaajig. Mii kina ooya enjigkendazig teg gechipiitendaagog sin. Yaawag dash wiigo debwetzigoog maanda gchitwaawendaagog dgog "Enjibwaajigeng". Gbaakogaade dash. Zaam gaa gegoo da-piitenziinaawaa. Wa dash edebwetang, gechitwaa'endang miinwaa mndaadendamowin eyaang dgomgad maanda, maage geyaabi go ngoji enjizhiwe-bag maanda, nsaaksin go maanda "Enjibwaajigeng" Dreamer's Rock.

Notes:

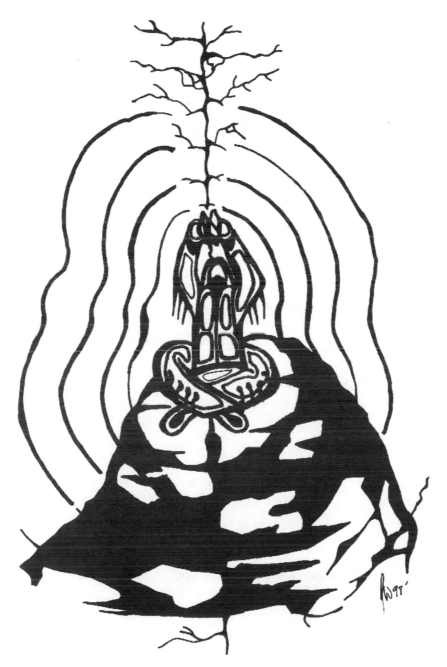

Sinmedwe'ek - Bell Rock

Sinmedwe'ek - Bell Rocks

8   A long time ago, the Ojibwe people were very respectful of everything on this Earth. Sinmedwe'ek - Bell Rocks was a gift to the Nishnaabeg from the Creator and Mother Earth. This gift, a sacred place, just as Enjibwaajigeng - Dreamers Rock, are places that render respect and reverence from those who come to these places. Sinmedwe'ek or Bell is what they used to call it, or "sounding rock". At one time there were eight rocks. The largest rock was in the middle. It was surrounded by the other rocks, which were set in a circle. This is how they were, at one time.

9   Along time ago, before the arrival of the whiteman, Sinmedwe'ek or Bell Rock was used by the Ojibwe people as a communication system. It was an early warning device used to signal others of impending attacks from warring nations from the south, or heralding the passing of a Lifelong chief. Or if there were any special occasion, they would sound the Bell. There were no telephones, no highways, the only form of communication or travel was the waterways. The bell rock sounded like a drum beating, the sound emanated from it could be heard all along the North shore area, and as far east as Nipissing, and to the south, almost as far as Parry Sound.

10   One time, along time ago, Sinmedwe'ek - Bell Rock were sounded, warning the Ojibwe people of an impending attack from the enemy, from the South. An enemy scouting party had been spotted travelling along east toward Sault Ste. Marie. The appearance of a scouting party usually meant that there was an army of warriors not far behind. Sinmedwe'ek were sounded, the scouting party was intercepted before Sault Ste. Marie, by the Ojibwe warriors. Of six men in the enemy party, only one was allowed to return to his people, with the expressed instructions to his people never to return to this area. This is an example of how the Sinmedwe'ek were used.

Sinmedwe'ek - Bell Rock

8 Mewzha, Jibwek aapji gii-mndaadendaanaawaa kina gegoo eteg gidkamig. "Sinmedwe'ek" miingowewziwin gii-aawan. Debendjiged Gzhe-Mnidoo miinwaa Shkakmikwe gaa-miinaajin Nishnaaben. Gii-gchitwaawendaagod dash maanda, dbishkoo go "Enjibwaajigeng". Aapji Nishnaabeg maampii bi-zhaajig mndaadendaanaawaa maanda. Siniin medwes'gin gii zhinkaadaanaawaan dash, "mcdwesing sin". Nshwaaswi ko gii-tenoon ninda siniin. Memoonjimchaag naanaawyihiing gii-te. Gaataayhing dash geyiin ni aanind gii-tenoon. Mii gaa-zhising ninda siniin gchi memzha.

9 Mcwzha, ji-bwaa-bi-dgoshing Waabshkiiycd, Siniinmedwe'egin Jibweg gii-nakaaznaawaan. Gii-dewe'aanaawaa sin wii-wiindmaagewaad iishpin ooya zhaawnong bi-njibaad waa-bi mookiitaagwaad. Maage wii-wiindmaagewaad ooya Gchi-gimaa gii-nbod. Gchi zhiwebag ge, mii mdwesjigeng. Gaa niinaa gegoo gii-tesnoo gngda-biiwaabkoonhs, gaa gegoo gchi miikanan. Mii go eta iw sin dewe-gaadeg waa-zhi-gnoonind ooya, maage ooya ngoji wii-zhaad iishpin mookzhoweng. Dbishkoo dewehgan, mii gaa nwewesing "Sinmedwe'ek". Waasa gii-ko-debtaagod, giiwednong nbiish teg biinash go Bawaakting, miinwaa oodi nikeyaa waabanong Niipsing, miinwaa zhaawnong Waasaaksing nikeyaa.

10 Ngoding, gchi mewzha, gii-mdwesjigaade "Sinmedwe'ek" wii-wiindmoond-waa gi Jibweg bi-yaanid Myaginishnaabeg (be baa nda miigaasjig) shaawnong nikeying wii-bi-mookiidwindwaa. Myaginishnaabeg ekawaabjig gii-waabmi-gaaswag mookshowewaad oodi Gchitwaa Maanii Ziibiing (Saint Mary's River), Bawaakting. Iishpin bi-zaagewewaad ekawaabjig, miigo geyii shkweyaang gi waa-bi-miigaasjig bi-yaawaad. "Sinmedwe'ek" gii-mdwesjigaade. Jibweg dash gii-ngaashmaawaan ni ekawaabjig oodi jibwaa dgoshnawaad Bawaakting. Gi dash ngodwaaswi gaa-ngaashmindwa, bezhig eta gii-bgidnaa wii-bskaabiid. Wii-wiind-maaged oodi gaa-bi-njibaad. Gaa wiikaa ji bi bskaabiiswaad maampii nikeyaa. Mii gaa-naabdak maanda "Sinmedwe'ek".

11 Sinmedwe'ek or Bell Rock were used for a lot of purposes, they were used for ceremonies a different times of the year. And where the Sinmedwe'ek - Bell Rocks are located there was a big town (village) there at one time. A lot of people lived in that area, a big town, that is the way it was, a lot of teepees, a lot of corrals, lots of horses. And they used to have ceremonies, at this place. Pow Wows and stuff like that.

12 Then one day, a big Trading Company came, they travelled by boat and stopped there to trade their stuff to the Native people for Furs and stuff like that. That is how they traded, they didn't use money. They often brought in what was needed very much, often Liquor too.

13 So, the young Ojibwe fellows were the only ones to drink it, nobody else, woman didn't drink it. One day, they went and stole the liquor, it had been expected, the liquor was in small kegs, that is what they stole, those young men. Except, that this time the Trading Company had poisoned the kegs of liquor. And the next morning, when the village awoke, when the people woke up. they seen the bodies of these young Ojibwe men lying all over the ground. That is what happened, those men at the Trading Company poisoned the kegs of liquor.

14 So, the Ojibwe people buried these young men right there, and there is a burial ground over there, where the Sinmedwe'ek - Bell Rock are. After that, the people dispersed, all moved away from there, some went to Wikwemikong, Killarney, Sagamok, Sheguiandah, West Bay and all the surrounding area. They abandoned that place altogether, nobody lives there now. Hasn't been for as long as I can remember, but they used to have a big town there.

15 Then one time, the Priests came to the Wiigwaaskingaa area. These people had not understood the Ojibwe people or the powers behind Sinmedwe'ek, it was suggested by these Priests, that Sinmedwe'ek were the result of an unearthly doing. They believed the Rock was evil. Because they believe this, they blessed the Sinmedwe'ek - Bell Rocks. This cause the sound to fade away.

11   Noonj go gii-naabdad wi "Sinmedwe'ek". Eyaapii go naa gegoo nakmagag, mii gii-dewe'gaadeg. Wi "Sinmedwe'ek" teg, gchi-odenaw gii-te ko. Gii-baatiinwag gaa-daajig maa gchi-odenaang. Niibna gii-tenoon wiigwaamesan, gii-baatiinwag bezhgoogzhiig, waakaaksijganan ge gii-tenoon. "Sinmedwe'ek" teg, mii maa gaa-nji-jiingtamwaad.

12   Ngoding dash giizhgak, emeshktoongejig gii-bi-dgoshnoog. Jiimaaning gii-bi-yaawag. Gii-bi-aashtoongewag. Noonj gegoo gii-biidoonaawaa. Nishnaaben dash gii-ndawendmaawaan wii-meshktoonmaagwaad mkindaaganan. Mii maanda gaa-zhi-aashtoongewaad. Gaawiin zhoonyaa gii-nakaazsiinaawaa. Aapji go waa-nakaazong mii gaa-biidoowaad. Shkodewaaboo ge gii-biidoonaawaa.

13   Miish go eta Jibwe niniwag czhkiniigjig gaa-mnikwejig. Gaa go geyaabi ooya. Gaawiin kwewag gii-mnikwesiiwag. Ngoding giizhgak gii-gmoodwag wi shkode-waaboo. Gii-dnenmigaaswag go. Gii-gaachnoon dash mkaksagoonhsing gii-biin-deg wi shkodewaaboo. Miish gaa-gmoodwaad gonda shkiniigshag. Enji meshtoongeng, mji-mshkiki maa gii-dgongaade shkodewaaboong. Eni waabang dash gshkoziwaad Nishnaabeg gii-waabmaawaan niibna Nishnaabenhsan eshkiniijig baamaangozowaad mtashkamig kina go ngoji. Mii i gaa-zhiwebak. Gi niniwag enjimeshiktoongeng gii-ziignaanaawaa mjimshkiki maa shkodewaaboong.

14   Mii go maa gii-ngokiiwaad gi Jibweg. Temgad dash go oodi ngokaan "Sinmedwe'ek" teg. Gaa-shkwaa-zhiwebak dash maanda gii-ni-maamaajaawag Nishnaabeg. Kina go gii-anjiiwag. Aanind gii-zhaawag Wikwemikong, Shiibaawnaaning, S'gamok, Sheguiandah, M'chigiing miinwaa go kina gaataay-hiing. Mii go pane gii-ngajgaadegban wi "Sinmedwe'ek" teg. Gaawiin ooya geyaabi daasii maa. Gaa go ooya gii-daasii maa eko mjimendmaa go. Aah, gchi-odenaw gii-te maa.

15   Ni'aa dash maanda gii-nshinaajtoon, Mekdekonye oodi Wiigwaaskingaa. Gaawiin gonda gii-nsistawaasiiwaan Jibwen maage iw gshkichgewin gaa teg oodi "Sinmedwe'ek". Maanda genh gii-kidwag gii-Mekdekonyeg, "naamkamig bi-njibaamgad iw enji mdwesing sin." Gii-mjigkendaanaawaa "Sinmedwe'ek". Mii dash maanda "Sinmedwe'ek" gaa-nji-nametamwaad. Gaawiin miinwaa aapji gii-gzhiiweszinoo "Sinmedwe'ek".

33

16   The last time, that I can remember hearing Sinmedwe'ek - Bell Rock, I was just a young boy maybe 4 or 5 years old. That time, my Grandfather and I were sitting outside our big square log house in the Old village, when we heard the drumming sound, like a loud pounding on a big hollow log. It was Sinmedwe'ek - Bell Rock. Someone, from Sheguiandah had come to ring the Rock. My Grandfather travelled by water to find out what had happened, one of the last Lifelong Chiefs had died, over there. Along time ago, they used to have Lifelong Chiefs on the reserves, they were Chiefs for life, not only for a couple of years. So, when this Chief passed away, the message was relayed all over. A lot of other people used the Bell Rock, they came from Killarney, S'gamok, Wikwemikong, Sheguiandah, M'chigiing and other places to use this early message centre, that what it was used for, but nobody ever lived there after what happened there, at Sinmedwe'ek.

Miigwech.

16   Shkwaach gii-noondmaa "Sinmedwe'ek" ngaachiinhnaaban iw pii, gnomaa naa niiwin maage naanan ngii-nsoboongis. Ngoding nmishoomis miinwaa niin naamd-abyaang gojiing gaa-daa'aang ekakdeyaag mtigamig ngii-noondaanaa dewegan dbishkoo go naa gchi mtig mdweganaajgaazod, ewiimbnakzid mtig. "Sinmedwe'ek" iw gii-aawan. Ooya Sheguiandah gii-bi-njibaa gaa-bi-mdwesdood iw "Sinmedwe'ek". Nmishoomis gii-mookshowe gii-oonda-gkenjiged gaa-zhiwe-bak. Mii iidig maaba bezhig shkwaach-ekobmaadzid-gimaa gaa-nbod, Sheguiandah oodi. Mewzha Jibweg gii-yaa'aawaan gimaan eko bmaadzid go gii-gimaawi maa shkonganing. Gaawiin go eta niizhobboon gii-gimaawsii. Miish maaba gimaa pii-nebod kina ooya gii-noondaan iw. Niibna bemaadzijig gii-nakaaznaawaa "Sinmedwe'ek". Oodi gaa-bi-njibaajig Shiibaawnaaning, S'gamok, Wikwemikong, Sheguiandah, M'chigiing, miinwaa go mziwe gii-nakaaznaawaa mewzha wiindmaagewin. Mii gaa-naabdak "Sinmedwe'ek". Gaa dash geyaabi ooya maa gii-daasii gaa-shkwaa-zhiwebak iw, oodi "Sinmedwe'ek" teg.

Miigwech.

Notes:

"Bgojinishnaabenh'sag"- Little People

Bgojinishnaabenhsag - Little People

17   A long time ago, my Great grandfather, Duncan McGregor went out on the Bay to set a fishing net. At that time, the place was wild around here. It was so wild that the trees, big Pine trees hung down over the waters edge. All the trees were rough and thick, there were snakes hanging over the trees, and over there, by the Point (McGregor Bay), this is where he set his net.

18   The next day, he left early in the morning to lift the net out of the water, and take the fish out. The Bay was very still, and was very misty that morning. The sun had just come up and everything was fresh and new. He paddled along, all was quiet, except for the sound of his paddle slapping the water, alongside the canoe. He paddled his canoe over to where he had set his net, pulled the net up out of the water, but there were no fish in it. So, he set the net again and went home. He went out again, the next day and again, there was no fish in the net. Again, he set the net, but this time, he hid in the thick trees hanging over the waters edge and waited. He waited for someone to come and lift his net and take the fish out.

19   Sure enough, by midnight, he heard voices, those Bgojinishnaabenhsag came along. They came in a little wee canoe. Those little people lifted the net and started to pull the fish out. Just then, the old man picked up a stone and threw it alongside their canoe, he called to them. Startled, they dropped the net right there, they started to paddle away, very fast. The old man called out to them, they wouldn't stop. So, the old man jumped into his canoe and raced after them.

20   Bgojinishnaabenhsag were very fast. They paddled right into an inlet. There was no way out for them. My Great Grandfather thought he had caught those little people. But those little people kept right on paddling, just as fast as they could, right straight toward a solid rock cliff. Just as those little people, in their little canoe, neared the wall of rock, one of them raised his paddle into the air and pointed it at the wall of rock. The rock cliff opened up and a passageway to the other side opened. In, went those little people in their little canoe, and they escaped, into the other bay.

"Bgojinishnaabenh'sag"- Little People

17 Mewzha, ngi chi-Mishoomis Duncan McGregor gii-oobgidwaa wiikwedong. Aapji gii-mtigwaakiiwan wi pii. Bgodkamig gchi zhingwaakoog gii-pkidgojinoog oodi nbiing. Kina mtigoog gii-gpagziwag miinwaa gii-gaapziwag. Gnebigoog gii-pkidgoojinoog mtigoong, oodi dash wiikwedong (McGregor Bay), mii maampii gii-bgidwaad.

18 Yaazhoo waabang, gchi kizhep gii-ni-maajaa wii-naadsabiid. Aapji gii-bzaanaagmisin wiikwed miinwaa aapji geyaabi gii-wan ekizhepbaawgag. Bjiinag gii-biidaaban miinwaa kina gegoo gii-shka'iiwan. Gii-zhebwe, kina ngoji gii-bzaante, mii go eta wzhebwaagan gaa-debwe'aagmiseg jiigi jiimaan. Gii-mookzhowe oodi gii-zhaad gaa-nji-bgidwaad. Gii-gwaabiignaan wdasabiiman, gaa dash ooya gii-goonh gii-yaasiiwan. Aanj miinwaa gii-bgidwaa. Mii dash gii-ni-giiwed. Gaa yaazho waabang aanj miinwaa gii-maajaa, gaa sa go ooya giigoonh. Mii sa miinwaa gii-aanji-bgidwaad. Noongo dash gii-kandwa oodi megwaakwaa. Gii-baabii'aan ooya wii-bi-naadsabiinid.

19 Oo geget, jiigyahiing yaabtaadibikak gii-noondwaan ooya giigdanid. Giiw Bgojinishnaabenhsag gii-bi-dgoshnoog. Aapji go gii-gaachin jiimaanenhs gii-bi-yaawaad. Bgojinishnaabenhsag gii-bi-naadsabiiwag. Mii dash iw pii ow kiwenziinh gii-daapnang sin gii-pagdood oodi jigi jiimaanwaa. Gii-gnoonaan dash. Aapji gii-gshkomaan, miigo gaa-zhi-bgijwebnaawaad sabiin maa, mii dash wewiip gii-maajiikzhowewaad. Kiwenziinh daa-ni-gnoonan, gaawiin dash gii-ngashziiwag. Mii dash kiwenziinh gii-bosegwaashknid wjiimaaning gii-bminaashkawaad.

20 Bgojinishnaabenhsag aapji gii-gwaashkweziwag. Getin gii-maajiikgzhowewag gyak wiikwedong. Gaawiin maamdaa wii-zaagjigshowewaad. Nendam genh ngi chi-Mishoomis mii sa ji debnagwaa gonda Bgojinishnaabenhsag. Pane gaa-namkoshwewaad, getin go, gyak maa giishkaapkak. Gonda Bgojinishnaabenhsag jiimaanenhswaang enidgoshnaawaad oodi giishkaapkak, bezhig wa ni'aa, wa nishnaabenhs gii-binan zhebwaagan mii dash maanda genh gii-shiwebnang (hand motion) gii-zhinooged oodi aasmaabik. Mii go gaa-zhi-nsaaksek maanda aazhbik. Mii go gaa-ni-zhi-zhiibaabiiyaag. Mii sa jiimaanenhswaan gii-nambideg gyak oodi zhiibaabiiyaag, oodi bezhig geyaabi wiikweyaak. Mii sa gii-zhaabwiiwaad.

21   My great grandfather thought that he too, could get through this passage to the other side, but it closed shut, right behind those little people. Even before the old man could manoeuvre his canoe toward it, it shut. He stopped his canoe at the rocks near the cliff, jumped out of his canoe and ran up to the top of the rock. By the time he got to the top, those Bgojinishnaabenhsag were already half way across the lake. So, he decided to leave them alone. He couldn't catch them anyway. He went home. That is one story about those Bgojinishnaabenhsag, those little wild men.

22   And another time, My son Tim had seen them too, when he was young, he was outside playing by himself and these little people were playing with him. They were out there laughing and playing, and when my wife asked him whom he was playing with he replied "oh my little friends". I don't know if he remembers that or not, but, he sure scared my wife. That is another story of these little guys. And my own Mother, when I was small used to say that as soon as it was getting dark, you had better get into the house and stay in the house cause those little men would come and get you. Sometimes, they would come and get children, to play with them.

23   Those little beings have been around this Earth for along time, and there are more of them, all over this country. But, you can't see them, sometimes, but they are around though. I don't know where they are. They never hurt anybody. And that's how the Native people learned how to make Maple Syrup.

24   Maple Syrup was being made here, in Canada, long before the Europeans came here. A long time before, Bgojinishnaabenhsag had, what most people describe as Telepathy. While we were sleeping, Bgojinishnaabenhsag told us how to make Maple Syrup. So, when we were told how to make it, we tried it and it worked. It's still being made today, but, it was those little wild men that told us how to do it.

25   Bgojinishnaabenhsag, they are around yet. If you loose something and you can't find it, you look all over the place, search all over and still can't find it, forget about it for awhile and go about your business, then all of a sudden it will turn up, it could be the work of those little wild men.

26   Thats how they work, they play tricks on people. That is the story of these little wild men. I don't know how they came about, but they are here among us, anyway. This is what they used to do and still do.   Miigwech.

21   Da-zhiibaakshowe geyii gii-nendam ngi chi Mishoomis. Gaa-shkwaa-zhiibaak-
shawewaad mii geyii kiwenziinh gii-bgamkoshwed maa zhiibaabiiyaag. Gii-
gbaakse dash zhiibaabiiyaag. Mii aani noopnanaad gii-btaasini oodi wjiimaan aasmaabik. Dowaaj dash gii-gwaashnjigwaashkni, gii-gidaakiiyeptoo. Miish oodi
gaa-dgoshing gidaabik gii-nimkoshwenid oodi aaptoogaam. Gii-booniikwaan
dash. Gaa wiin gii-gshkitoosiin wii-debnaad. Gii-ni-giiwe. Mii wi bezhig
Bgojinishnaabehnsag aadsokaan.

22   Ngooding ge go, ngwis, Tim go gewiin gii-waabmaan, epiichi gaachiinhid.
Nshike gojiing gii-damno, mii gonda Bgojinishnaabensag gii-wiidookwaawaan
niw. Gii-yaawag gojiing wiidookaaswaad miinwaa baabaapwaad. Nwiidgemaagan
gii-gwejmaan wenesh ewiidookwaajin. Tim gii-kida "nwiichkewensag". Gaawiin
ngi-gkendaziin endgwenh ji mjimendang Tim wi. Gii-zegigoon wiigo
Nwiidgemaagan . Mii go wi bezhig Bgojinishnaabensag dbaajmowin. Nmamaa,
gii-gaachiinhyan ko gii-kida, ni dbikak, shki dbikak aabdig wii-bi-biindigeng,
biindig wii-yaayan. Gdaa-bi-naangoog nii giw Bgojinishnaabenhsag.
Naangodnoong dash maajiinaawaan binoojiinhan wii-wiidookwaawaad.
23   Gchi mewzha go gonda Bgojinishnaabenhsag bi ko yaawaad mampii gidkamig.
Kina go mziwe yaawag. Naangodnoong gaawiin gdoo waabmaasiig, yaawag dash
wii go. Gaawiin ngigkendamaasiig yaawaad. Gaawiin ooya bbaamendmaasii-
waan. Mii ninda Nishnaabeg gaa-kinoomaagwaajin waa zhi-ziisbaakdokewaad.
24   Ninaatigo-ziiwaagbmide gii-zhickgaade maampii Canada jibwaa dgoshnawaad
goonda Waabshkiiyejig gchi gaaming bi njibaajig. Mewzha, Bgojinishnaabensag
gii-yaanaawaa niigaan-nendmowin, noongo ezhinikaadeg "telepathy". Epiichi
nbaaying, Bgojinishnaabensag kii-wiindamaagnaanik waa-zhi-zhitooying
ninaatigo-ziiwaagbmide. Kii-wjitoonaa, gii-nakiimgad dash go. Noongo go
geyaabi zhichgaade ninaatigo-ziwaagbmide. Mii gonda bgoji-niniwag gaa
zhichgewaad, gaa-zhi-kinoomaagyiing.
25   Bgojinishnaabenhsag, yaawag go geyaabi. Iishpin gegoo wnitooyan, gaawiin
mkaswan, kina go ngoji gdoo ndawaab, gaawiin dash go gmakziin, wnendan jina,
paanankiin go enakiimban, gchi geskana go gbi mi mkaan, gnomaa mii gonda
Bgojinishnaabennsag dankiiwniwaa.
26   Mii gonda ezhchigewaad, gwii-nda-weshsagoog. Gii-zhiingengdaagziinhwag.
Mii maanda enaajmindwaa gonda bgoji-niniwag. Manj iidig gaa-zhi-daadziwaag-
wenh, yaawag sa wii go maampi. Mii ko maanda gaa nankiiwaad, geyaabi go
noongo.   Miigwech.

Notes

Ninaatigo-Ziiwaagbmide - Maple Syrup

Akinini - Earth Man

27 Akinini, the Earth man, was a little boy at one time, just a little boy about seven years old. He was a kind of a Spirit boy. One day, while he was playing by the waters edge, a spirit came to him. The spirit wanted to know how much food the people in the village had, and then, Akinini wondered why the Spirit wanted to know about the amount of food the village had.

28 The Spirit told him that in a couple of days time, they would have to move the village out of there, out into the country, elsewhere, far away. Akinini did not pay much attention to the Spirit, until the scouts, there used to be scouts where ever there was a settlement, they had two or three scouts, anyway, these scouts came in and told everyone that they were going to have to move out of there. Just as the Spirit had told Akinini, that the people and the village would have to move, for the enemy are coming with their raiding party. So, they got ready.

29 Akinini, got ready to move, just as the Spirit predicted and instructed him to do. Akinini gave the people of the village instructions. They were told to tie all the canoes together, one behind the other, each of you get in and tie a blindfold over your eyes. So, the village people all got ready that day, and that night each had a blindfolds on. Soon, all those who were wearing blindfold could hear the rushing of water alongside the canoes, they were not paddling or anything, they were all blindfolded, they didn't know where they were going, but the were going swiftly. They travelled all night like that. The next morning, they could hear the canoes plow up into sand, somewhere along the shore. Then, they took off their blind-folds, at daylight, they saw lots of trees around and some wild animals. They saw where they were. Thats where they lived. In the meantime, the enemy had raided the place that the people had just left and they couldn't find any of the people from that village.

Akinini - Earth Man

27 Akinini, gwiiwzenhs gii-aawi ngoding, aapji go egaachiinhid gwiiwzenhs, gnomaa naa niishwaaswi gii-nso-boongiswidik. Gii-Mnidoo-endaagzi maaba gwiiwzenhs. Ngoding giizhgak, epiichi damnod jiigbiig, Mnidoon gii-bi-disgoon. Mnidoo wii-nda-gkendaan mnik miijin e-yaamwaad oodenwesing bemaadzijig. Aaniish iidig, nendam maaba Akinini, waa-nji-nda-gkendang maaba Mnidoo mnik eyaamwaad miijim odenwensing.

28 Mnidoo gii-wiindmaagoon, ni niizhgongag, aabdig ji-aanjiiwaad, ngoji bkaan ji-oodaawaad, ji-aandkiiwaad, ngoji go waasa. Akinini gii-baamtoowaasiin, baamaa go e-kawaabid (e-kandood); e-kawaabjig gii-yaawag niish maage nswi enso teg go oodenaw, gii-bi-zhaawag dash gonda, gii-bi-wiindmaagewag aabdig ji-aandoodegozid kina ooya. Mii maanda gaa-bi-gopan Akinini niw Mnidoon, wii-aandodegoziwaad kina go bemaadzijig endaajig maa oodenwesing. "Myaginishnaabeg kwii-bi-mookiitaagonaanik". Mii dash gii-zhiitaawaad.

29 Akinini gii-zhiitaa wii-aanjiid, gaa-kidod sa gonaa wa Baagaak miinwaa gaa naad wii-zhichgenid. Akinini gii-windmawaan Nishnaaben oodenwesing waazhichgewaad wii-aandodegziwaad. Gii-kida "Aankoopdoon kina jiimaanan, bebezhig. Ka-boozim, ka-gbiingwebnidzom dash". Mii dash giizhgak gii-zhiitaawaad, enidbikak kina ooya gbiingwebzo. Kina dash go egbiingwebzojig wiiba go gii-noondmowaad ni maajiishkaanik ni jiimaaman. Gmaapii ggwetaankamik genh epiichbideg mii go eta mdwedjiwang jiigi jiimaanwaa ziiba, nbiish. Gaawiin wii go dankaasiinaawaan zhebwaaganan, kina gii-gbingwebzowag. Gaa-ggkendziinaawaa ezhaawaad. Zhaawag sii go ngoji. Mii go gbedibik gaa-zhibmiyaawaad. Miish bi mi waaseyaabang, jiigyahiing biidaabang, mii gii-jekbideg ni jiimaanan jiigbiik, nookdaawngaak. Gii-giichwebnaanaawaan gbiingwebzownan gaa-ni-waase 'aabang. Gii-waabmaawaan niibna mtigoon miinwaa niibna wesiinhan. Mii gii-waambdamwaad yaawaad. Mii maa gaa daawaad. Epiichi zhiwebak dash maanda, Myaginishnaabeg (be baa nda miigaasjig) dash gii-oomookiitaanaawaa Jibwek gaa-ngadmoowaad oodenwens. Gaawiin dash ooya giimkawaasiiwaan gonda Myaginishnaabeg (be baa nda miigaasjig) ninda Nishaaben ednakiipiniin maa.

30   Akinini, the Earth man had already been given instructions by the Spirit, and had already informed the village of the move, so they moved. And Akinini, I don't know how he did it, but, he made those canoes move along the water and the paddles were right there, inside the boats, no one used them. Morning came, and they were already far away from their old village. They lived at the new village site for along time.

31   Akinini got old. The people grew very old, too. He told the people of the village, that he would leave soon. When you see me dead, look for the high ground over there. Put me there, cover me with a blanket. When the time came, that is what they did. They went to look for the highest spot and laid Akinini there. Covered him with a blanket and left him there. Three days later, they thought it odd, that there was no smell of a corpse coming from that spot. So, one of them was brave enough to go and lift that blanket. There was nobody there. Akinini, just completely disappeared. All they saw was a mound of earth in the shape of a body. Akinini had turned back into earth. That is what happened to him. And that is the story of the Earth man.

Miigwech

30 Akinini, zhaashgo gaa-wiindmaagaazod waa-zhichgeng, mii gii-aandodegzi-waad gonda Nishnaabeg. Manj iidig gaa-zhi-gshkitoogwenh Akinini wii-maaji-ishkaamgak jiimaanan ggetin gidbiig. Zhebwaaganan ge biinji jiimaaning gii-tenoon, Gaa ooya gii-nakaaziinan. Ewaabang sa wiigo waasa gii-dgoshnoog, gaa-njibaawaad gete oodenaang. Mii maa shki oodenaang gaa-daawaad gbeyiing.

31 Akinini gii-ni-gkaa. Gii-ni-gkaawag gonda Nishnaabeg gewiinwaa. Miish gii-wiindmawaad, mii shigo wii maajaad. Pii nboyaanh, nda-waambdamoog mkok-migaag oodi. Mii maa ji-siyeg. Ka-maandgonwim waabowaan. Gaa-memkaaj ka-niibaabsiim. Pii-nebod, mii gaa-zhichgewaad. Gii-ndawaambdaanaawaa shpaak mkokmigaag. Mii maa gii-saawaad Akininwan. Gii-maandagonwaawaan waabowaan, mii maa gii-nganaawaad. Miish genh eni-nsognagak, gii-maamkaadenmoog, gaa-genaa-biijmaagozisii wa gaa-nbod. Miish bezhig e-aakde'ed gii-zhaad oodi gii-baakiignamwaad wi waabowaan. Gaa dash genh maa ooya gii-yaasii. Mii go bekaa gaa-zhi-ngoshkaad. Mii go eta gaa-waabndang mkokmigaag. Dbishkoo gonaa ooya zhngishing. Akinini, gii-bskaabi gaa-bi-njibaad. Mii sa gewii gaa-zhiwebzid wa. Mii wi Akinini aadsookaan.

Miigwech

Notes:

Pahiinsag - River Dweller

"Pahiinsag" - River Dweller

32 Pahiinsag are little people that live along the rivers edge or shorelines. They are called Pahiinsag or "river dweller". If you don't bother them, they won't bother you at all. You would see them, these little wee things walking along the shore. Don't bother them, just travel or do what your supposed to be doing.

33 And with the story of the Earth man, Akinini, there is a little part of that story, too. Akinini, was kind of lazy, he didn't want to do much. He was sitting up there at the fire house, eating his meals, he didn't even cook, he let others do the cooking. So, one day, he went with a hunting party, they went up north, travelling a couple of days, when they came upon Pahiinsag at this place along the shore by the river. Akinini cautioned those members of the hunting party not to bother those little people. But there was one bold man, he started to chase those little people away, so he began to cause trouble.

34 Akinini told the hunting party that they would have to leave right away, they have to keep going right now. This man is causing trouble, so they all left. They followed the river inland. They were starting to get hungry, they could not find anything to eat. Those little people chased all the animals away, not even any fish, there. Members of the hunting party were getting very hungry, they wanted to know what to do.

35 So, Akinini and the hunting party travelled inland, and he found some Prairie groundhogs, a little animal that lives on the prairies. These animals can dig fast, when they see someone coming they dig a way out into the ground, right away, quick. These Prairie ground hogs are fast. And this guy, the Earth man, just walks right up and pounds them on the head. He got three or four of these groundhogs, cooked them up and these animals are quite filling. Nobody else, could do this. When he walked, it looked as if the ground were shrinking underneath him. Thats how fast he was. And he was even known to catch wild Buffalo that is how fast he was.

Pahiinsag - River Dweller

32 Pahiinsag, aapji e-gaachiinhjig bemaadzijig gonda aawag jiigbiig maage gami-ing endaadjig. Mii Pahiinsag enji zhinkaazwaad, gamiing ednisjig. Iishpin bbaamendmaaswaadwaa, gaa geyiin ka-bbaamendmigsiik. Gdaa-waabmaag gonda e-gaachiinhjig bmasewaad jiigbiig. Gego bbaamendmaake gi ka-mishkaa go eta maa jiigahiing. Gego bbaamendmaake, gdaa-zhichge megwaa ezhchigenhban iishpin mi zhiibaashkaayan maa, ka-mookzhowe, mi zhiibaakzhowe'iin maa, ka-zhiibbaakzhowe go eta.

33 Maaba dash enaajmind Akinini, geyiin go ni dbaade maampi wi. Gii-gtimaadzi Akinini, gaawiin aapji gegoo gii-nankiisii. Gii-nmadbi oodi shkodegamgong, waawiisni. Gaa go wiin gii-jiibaakwesii. Ooya go naa gii-bgidnaan wii-jiibaak-wenid. Ngoding giizhgak gii-baa-wiijiiwe baa ndawenjigeng giiwednong. Eko niizhgongag mii gii-bmi-waabmaawaad Pahiinsan gamiing. Akinini dash gii-gnamoohaan wii bwaa-bbaamendmaawaad ni Pahiinsan. Bezhig dash maaba nini gii-msawendam, gii-konaashkowaan ni Pahiinsan. Mii dash maa gii-maazhiiwiid.

34 Akinini gii-naan ni nendawendjgenjin, "Aabdig wewiib wii-ni-maajaahiing. Noongo go wewiib. Maaba nii naa bezhig nini bnaajchige. Miish gii-ni-maa-jaawaad. Gii-naagdoonaawaa wi ziibi. Gmaapiich gii-bkadewag. Gaa gego gii-mkaziinaawaa waa-miijwaad. Gi egaachiinjig nishnaabensag gii-kon-aashkowaawaan kina wesiinhan. Gaa waawaaj go ooya giigoonh. Miish gonda nendawendjgejig, aapji pkadewag. Wii-nda-gkendaanaawaa waa-zhichgewaad.

35 Akinini, miinwaa gi giiwseniniwag, gii-bmasewag go, eshkam go waasa noop-ming gii-ni-dgoshnoog. Miish wesiinhsan gii-ni-waabmaawaad mshkodeng endaajig. Aapji dash gonda kookjiishag ntaa waankewag. Iishpin ooya bi-yaanid mii go wewiib waasa go naankewaad. Jepziwag aapji. Miish maaba Akinini, naaskowaad baagndibeganaamaad. Gnomaa naa nswi maage niiwin, gii-debnaan, gii-mnaswaawaan. Mii sa gii-debsiniiwaad gaa-shkwaa-jiibaakwewaad. Gaa go ooya daa-gshkitoosiin wi gaa-piichi-gzhiikaad maaba Akinini. Dbishkoo go naa daapshkaag wi ki mii gaa-piichi-piichbisod. Bgoji-bzhikoon ge go gii-dimnewaan gii-debinaan, mii gaa-piichi-jepzid wa Akinini.

36   These Pahiinsag are another kind of little wild people. They live close by rivers and shorelines, fishing and everything else. They never go inland, they stay close by the river. And these little guys, you don't touch them, for if you do, then watch out, for they will attack you, too.

37   All those stories, Akinini, Pahiinsag, Bgojinishnaabensag, are true stories. There are a lot of these stories about these little guys and Louis Migwanabe, old William Andrew's father, he used to have a lot of stories to tell and he was a good story-teller.

Miigwech.

36　Bkaanziwag go gewiinwaa gonda Pahiinsag. Jiigbiig gonda daawag, gii-gii-goonhkewag ge. Gaa-wiikaa-gpiisiiwag. Bezha go ziibiing baa-yaawag. Gaa dash gonda gdaa-bbaamenmaasiik. Iishpin zhichgeyan wi, miigo gdaa-mookiitaagook go.

37　Ninda dbaajmownan, Akinini, Pahiinsag, Bgojinishnaabensag debwemgadoon go. Baatiindoon go ninda dbaajmownan, Pahiinsag maage Bgojinishnaabensag. Louis Miignobi (Migwanabe), zhinkaazo bezhig Nishnaabe, Wiiyam Andrews oosan, niiba dbaajmownan gii-yaanan. Aapji gii-ntaa-dbaajmo. Gii-ntaa-aansooke wa kiwenziinh.

Miigwech

Bibliography

Baraga, Frederic. A Dictionary of the Ojibwe Language. St. Paul: Minnesota Historical Society Press, Revised Edition. 1992.

Barry, James. Georgian Bay. Toronto: Clark, Irwin & Co. Ltd. 1968.

Bishop, C.A. The Northern Ojibwe and The Fur Trade: A Historical and Ecological Study. Toronto: Holt Rinehart and Winston of Canada, 1974.

Greenman, E. F. Old Birch Island Cemetery. Ann Arbor: University of Michigan Press, 1951.

Gutsche, A.,et al. The North Channel and St. Marys River : A Guide to History. Toronto : Lynx Images, 1997.

Henry, Alexander Travels and Adventures. Chicago: Lakeside Press, 1921.

Johnston, Basil Ojibwe Language Lexicon. Public Documents, Department of Ethnology, Royal Ontario Museum.1978.

Morse, E. W. Fur Trade Canoe Routes of Canada / Then and Now. Public Documents, 1969.

New, W. H. Native Writers and Canadian Writing: Canadian Literature Special Issue. Vancouver: University of British Columbia Press, 1990.

Patterson II, E. P. The Canadian Indian: A History Since 1500. Don Mills: Collier - Macmillan, 1972.

Petrone, Penny Native Literature in Canada: From Oral Tradition to the Present. Toronto: Oxford University Press, 1990.

Pitawankwat, et.al. The History of Birch Island. Unpublished. 1978.

Rhodes, Richard A. Eastern Ojibwa-Chippewa-Ottawa Dictionary. New York, Berlin: Mouton de Gruyter, 1993.

Shmalz, P.S. The Ojibwe of Southern Ontario. Toronto: University of Toronto Press, 1991.

Fiero Orthography

The writing system that is used, is called the Fiero Orthography. It was devised by C. E. Fiero, and this format is used to differentiate sounds in the Ojibwe language, to specifically identify differences.

Example :	gamiing	-	across the lake
	gaaming	-	by the lake

Ojibwe has seven main vowels: short a, short i, and short o, three long vowels paired with the short ones, and an unpaired long vowel e. Using Fiero orthography the long vowels are distinguished from the paired short vowels by being written double: a and aa, i and ii, o and oo; the unpaired e is left unmarked.

Fiero Orthography - Vowels

Short vowels -   i, (zhigo) ; a, (pane) ; o, (dgoshin)
Long vowels -   ii, (niin) ; aa, (maajaa); oo,(tenoon); e, (shkode)

Fiero Othography - Consonants

b, d, g, j, z, zh, p, m, t, n, k, ch, s, sh, w, y,

In the Ojibwe Language, the differences in vowel sounds are as follows: the right side Ojibwe vowel sounds and on the left the English vowel equivalent sounds.

Ojibwe Vowel Sounds (Long)		English Vowel Sounds (Long)
ii - wiigwas	=	ee - week
aa - maajaa	=	a - mall
oo - noonga	=	oo - look
e - enjibaa	=	e - net
Short		Short
a - gamiing	=	u - gum
i - nini	=	i - bit
o - ngoji	=	ou - out

Glossary - Ojibwe to English

Other sounds

Nasal n   =   nh - gehn,   n middle - genzh
Glottal stop ' (catch in the throat) e'aakde'ed
Sometimes use h =   ehaakdehed

Grammatical Terms

vai	-	intransitive with animate subject
vii	-	intransitive with inanimate subject
vta	-	verb transitive animate
vti	-	verb transitive inanimate
na	-	noun animate
ni	-	noun inanimate
av	-	adverb
pn	-	pronoun
pv	-	preverb

Note: Some enties in the Ojibwe - English Glossary are entered as Root word verbs, either the verb animate or inaminate, transitive or intransitive. Some of thes entries come directly from the dictionary (Eastern Ojibwe-Chippwa-Ottawa Dictionary). Some words appear in plural or singular form. The addition of a prefix or suffix, or a change in sentence structure (context the verb is used) may alter the verbs grammatical structure.

Entries may appear with different spellings and pronunciation, for some Ojibwe speakers, since there are several distinct dialect variations in and around Great Lakes regions.

Some words appear in this order:

Example   mookzhowe   - to paddle (root word)
                              - ng, paddling
                              - waad, they paddle (plural ending)
                  mookzhoweng - paddling
                  mookzhowewaad - they paddle

Glossary - Ojibwe to English

aabdig	- for sure - (av)
aabji	- ever - (av)
aadsookaan	- sacred story - (na)
aandkiiwaad	- (they) change residence - (vti)
aandoodegozid	- (they) going to move to another location - (vti)
aaniish	- how - (av)
aanind	- some, other people - (ni)
aanj	- again - (av)
aanji	- over again (av)
aanjiid	- move again - (vai)
aanjiiwaad	- move elsewhere (again) - (vta)
aankanootaanaawaa	- (they) translated - (vai)
aankanootmowaad	- interpret (they) - (vai)
aankanootmowaawaa	- came to translate for him - (vai)
	- n, translate for them
aankoopdoon	- tie together (in a chain) - (vti)
aapji	- very - (pv) - go, - very much
aaptoogaam	- halfway across the lake - (av)
aashtoongewaad	- they traded - (vta) - refer to meshkdoonaad
aashtoongewag	- come to trade - (vta)
aasmaabik	- the side of the rock (cliff) - (av)
aawaad	- are to be - (vai), (pl)
aawan	- it is - (vai)
aawi	- to be - (vai) - d, be a certain person or thing - (vai)
aazhbik	- rock - (ni)
aazhbikong	- on the rock - (av)
Akinini	- Earthman - (na)
baabaapwaad	- they are laughing, (all) - (vti)

baabii'aan	- wait for - (vta)
baagaakwaan	- spirits of - (na)
baagaakwag	- spirits - (na)
baagndibeganaamaad	- hits them on the head (hard) - (vta)
baakiignamwaad	- uncovered (someone) - (vta)
baakiignang	- turn down; uncovered - (vti)
baamaa	- later - (av)
baamaangozowaad	- laying on the ground (plural) - (vti)
baataashin	- caught, trapped - (vai)
baatiindoon	- a lot, lots of (something) (an.) - (vta)
baatiinhaad	- a lot, lots of (something) (an.) - (vta)
bangii	- a little, a little bit - (ni)
Bawaakting	- place - Sault Ste. Marie - (na)
bbaamaadziwaad	- travel -(they) - (vai)
bbaamendmaa	- bother someone - (vta)
bbaamendmaake	- don't bother (them) - (vta)
bbaamendmaasiik	- leave them alone - (vta)
bbaamendmaasiiwaan	- (they) don't bother nobody - (vta)
bbaamendmaaswaadwaa	- (if) you don't bother them - (vta)
bbaamendmaawaad	- bother them - (vta)
bbaamtawaad	- listen to what someone says - (vta)
bbaamtoowaasiin	- didn't listen - (vta)
bebezhig	- one at a time, one by one - (av)
bekaa	- quietly, take it slow - (av)
bemaadzid	- live - (vai)
bemaadzijig	- people - (na)
bemaadziwin	- living - (vai)
besho	- near, close, - (av) also jiigi (pn)

bezhgoogzhii	- horse - (na)
bezhig	- one - (nm)
bgamkoshwed	- arrive by rowing (vai)
bgidnaad	- allow someone to do something - (vta)
bgidnang	- let go of something - (vti)
bgidniged	- make an offering - (vai)
bgidnigeng	- offered (what they gave) - (vai)
bgidnigeyan	- offer (what you want) - (vta)
bgidwaad	- set one's net - (vai)
bgijwebnaawaad	- dropped something, let fall - (vta)
bgodkamig	- in the wilderness (av)
bgoji	- wild - (vai)
bgoji bzhikoon	- wild cow (buffalo) - (na)
bgoji ninwag	- wild men (pl) - (na)
Bgojinishnaabenhsag	- little wild Indians - (na)
bgosendang	- hope - (vai)
bgosendmaad	- what he hoped (vai)
bgosendmindwaa	- request of someone (pl) -(vta)
bi	- come and (do something) - (pv)
biidaaban	- sunrise - (av)
biidoonaawaa	- they brought (plural) - (vta)
biidoowaad	- brought (something to someone) - (vta)
biijmaagzisii	- does not smell - (vai)
biimskomo	- spiral, goes around - (vii)
biinash	- until - (av)
biinde	- inside container - (av)
biindig	- inside (somewhere) - (av)
biindigeng	- come inside - (vai)

Glossary - Ojibwe to English

biinji	- inside of (something) - (pn)
binaangoog	- they would come for you - (vai)
binoojiinh'an	- children - (na)
bjiinag	- just (a short time ago) - (av)
bkaan	- different - (av)
bkaanziwag	- be different - (av)
bkade	- hungry - (vai)
bkadewag	- were hungry - (vai)
bmaseyan	- by walking (sing.) - (vai)
bmazewaad	- they walk - (vai)
bmi	- going past - (pv)
bminaashkawaad	- chased - (vta)
bmishkaad	- go along in a boat - (vai)
bmosed	- walk (along) - (vai)
bnaajtood	- ruin something, spoil - (vii)
bnaanjchige	- destroys - (av)
booniikwaan	- leave someone alone - (vta)
boozigwaashknid	- hopped on, get on - (vai)
bskaabiid	- come back - (vai)
bskaabiidwaad	- to come back (pl) - (vai)
btaaksini	- hit against something (his/hers) - (vai)
bwaa	- not - (pv)
bwaadang	- dream about something - (vta)
bwaadmowaad	- dreamt (they) - (vii)
bwaajge	- dream - (vai)
bwaajgejig	- dreamt (those who) - (vai)
bwaajgewaad	- dreamed (they) - (vai)
bwaajgewin	- dream - (na) - an, dreams

bzaanaagmisin — still (water) - (av)

bzaante — it is quiet - (av)

da — might, - future tense

daa — would, - future tense

daa'aang — where we live - (vai)

daabshkaag — shrink away - (vai)

daad — live in a certain place - (vai)

daadziwaagwenh — where did they come from - (av)

daapnang — picked up (something) - (vti)

daasii — does not live - (vai) - maa, not live there

daawag — (they) live in a certain place - (vai)

damnod — plays - (vai)

dasabiimon — his net - (ni)

dash — then, variation, Mii dash; mii-sh - (av)

dbaajmo — narrate (tell) - (vai) - win, story - (na)

dbaajmotwaad — tell about something (someone) - (vai)

dbaajmownan — tell stories - (vai)

dbikak — evening - (av)

debendang — one who owns something - (vti)

debendjged — one who owns (Master) - (vta)

debenjgenjin — variation "debendjged"

debnaan — caught (catch something) - (vta)

debnagwaa — catch them - (vta)

debsinii — be full (from eating) - (vai) - waad, they are full

debtang — heard something in the distance - (vti)

debwe'aagmiseg — paddle through the water (sound) - (vii)

debwe'esing — sound in the distance - (vii)

debwemgadoon — believe to be true (these) - (vai)

debwetzigoog   - those who disbelieve - (vta)

debwewendang   - believe in something - (vta)

dewe'gaadeg   - to beat something, (to drum) - (vai)

dewehgan   - drum - (na)

dgog   - is there (be in a certain place naturally) - (vii)

dgomgag   - that there is - (vii)

dgon'ged   - mix - (vai)

dgongaade   - mixed with; put in - (vti)

dgoshnan   - you arrive there - (vai)

dgoshnawaad   - (they) arrive (pl) - (vai)

dgoshning   - arrive (you) - (vai)

dgoshnoog   - arrive (pl) - (vai)

dibishkoo   - just like, as if (same) - (av)

dimnewaan   - to catch up, overtake - (vta)

disgoon   - appear before someone - (vta)

dkamkoshwewaad   - go across the water by canoe - (vii)

dnendam   - to expected - (av)

dnendang   - expect something to be in a certain place - (vti)

dnenjigaade   - it was expected - (av)

dnenmigaaswag   - expects (plural) - (vta)

e "aakde"ed   - brave - (av)

edebwetang   - one who believes - (vta)

ednakiipiniin   - ones who used to reside there (pl) - (vai)

ednizjig   - ones who live in a certain place - (vai)

egaachiinhid   - be small - (vai)

egbiingwebzojig   - those with blindfolds - (vta)

ekakdeyaag   - square - (av)

ekawaabid   - look out - (vai)

ekizhepbaawgag	- in the early morning - (av)
eko	- as long as, since - (pv)
eko mjimendmaa	- (as long as) I can remember - (vta)
ekobemaadzid	- lifelong - (av)
enaajmind	- what is told about someone (sing.) - (vta)
enaajmindwaa	- what is told about someone (pl) - (vta)
enankiimban	- (what) you were doing - (vti)
endaad	- where he dwells, at his home - (vai) - jig, where they live
endgwenh	- I wonder (whether) - (av)
enidbikak	- in the evening - (av)
enidgoshnaawaad	- when they got there - (vta)
enji	- why - (pv)
enjibaajig	- where one comes from - (vai)
Enjibwaajigeng	- place, Dreamers Rock - (na)
cnjigkendazig	- why, he doesn't know - (vai)
enjizhiwebag	- why it happens - (vai)
enso	- every - (av)
epiichbideg	- how fast its going - (av)
epiichi	- while - (pv)
eshkam	- more and more, gradually - (av)
eta	- only - (av)
ewaabang	- in the morning - (av)
eyaapii	- once in a while - (av)
ezchigewaad	- what they are doing - (vai)
ezhaawaad	- where they are going - (vai)
ezhchigehban	- what you are doing - (vai)
ezhkiniigjig	- young people, youth - (na)

ezhnikaadeg	- what it is called - (vai)
ezhpaapkaag	- high rock (stone) - (na)
ga	- future tense - (pv)
gaa	- no, not, (gga, variation) - (av) - wii, no not - wiin, no
gaa gegoo	- nothing - (av)
gaachiinhyan	- I was small - (vai)
gaachin	- small - (vii)
gaaming	- across the lake - (av)
gaapziwag	- rough - (av)
gaataayhiing	- all around - (av)
gbaakogaade	- it is closed (locked) (vii)
gbedibik	- all night - (av)
gbeyiing	- a long time - (av)
gbiingwebzo	- blindfolded - (vai) - zom, blindfolded
gbiingwebzom	- blindfolded (they) - (vai)
gbiingwebzowag	- were blindfolded - (vai)
gbiingwebzownan	- blindfolds - (vai)
gchi	- great, big, (pn)
Gchi mishoomis	- Great Grandfather - (na)
gchitwaa	- sacred, honorable (holy) - (vai)
Gchitwaa Maanii Ziibiing	- place St. Mary's River - (na)
gchitwaawendaagod	- sacred (holy) - (vai) - oon, holy things - (na)
gchitwaawendaagog	- what is sacred (holy) - (vai)
gchitwaawendang	-holy spiritual (one) - (na)
gchitwaawzid	- be respected - (vai)
gdaa	- you could - (pv)
gdaagiigin	- cloth - (na)

gdoo	- yours - (second person)
ge	- and - (pv)
ge nii	- me too - (pn)
gechipiitendaagog	- what is held in high esteem, great - (vai)
gechipiitzid	- Elder - (na)
gechipiitzijig	- Elders - (na)
gechipiitzinjin	- Elders - (na)
gechitwaa'endang	- think it is sacred - (vai)
gegaa	- nearly - (av) - go, almost
geget	- for sure - (av)
gegoo	- something, anything, - (ni)
genh	- so the story goes, (yeah right) what someone says to register disbelief - giiwenh variation - (av)
geskana	- all of a sudden, - (av)
gete	- very old, ancient - (pn)
gewii manda	- this one too - (av)
gewiin	- you too variation ge'e - (na) - waa, they too - (pn)
geyaabi	- yet , still - (av)
geyii	- you - (na) - n, you too - (pn)
ggetin	- very hard - (av)
ggizheb	- early morning - (av)
ggwejmaa	- ask someone something - (vta)
ggwetaani	- extremely - (pv)
ggwetaankamig	- extremely - (av)
gidaa	- up, on - (av)
gidaabik	- on top of rock (steel) - (av)
gidaabkong	- on top of rock (steel) - (av)
gidaakii'eptoo	- run uphill - (vai)

Glossary - Ojibwe to English

gidaakiiyegaadewse	- going uphill by walking - (vai)
gidkamig	- on earth - (av)
gii	- (pv) past tense
giichwebnaanaawaan	- tossed, took off something - (vta)
giigda biiwaabkoonhs	- telephone (speaking wire) - (ni)
giigdanid	- hear someone talking - (vai)
giigdod	- to speak in a certain way - (vai)
giigoonh	- fish - (na) - ked, fished - (vai)
giigoonhkewag	- they fished (vai)
giin	- you - (pn)
giishkaapkak	- rockcut - (na)
giitaabwag	- sit in a circle - (vai)
giiwed	- to go home - (vai)
giiwednong	- in the North - (av)
giiwseniniwag	- hunters - (vai)
giizhgak	- be day, daytime - (vii)
giizhiitaad	- finished doing something - (vai)
giizhik	- cedar - (na)
giji	- on (top of something) (av)
gijyahiing	- on top (av)
Gimaa	- boss, Chief - (na)
gimaawi	- to be chief - (vai)
Gimaawid	- be Chief - (vai)
Gimaawsii	- was not Chief - (vai)
gjitoonaa	- we tried it, tested it - (vti)
gkaa	- old - (vai)
gkaawag	- (they) got old - (vai)
gkendaan	- to find out, to know - (vti)

gkendaanaawaa	- try to know - (vai)
gkendamaasiig	- don't know (they) - (vta)
gkendang	- to know (knew) - (vti)
gkendaziin	- doesn't know - (vta)
gkendziinaawaa	- they don't know - (vta)
gkenjige	- to know, find out something - (vta)
gkenmaawaad	- want to know something about him - (vta)
gkenmaawaad	- to know - (vai)
gkenmind	- was known - (vai)
gmaapii	- after a long time, in a while - (av) - j, later on, afterwards
gmakziin	- can't find - (vai)
gmishkaa	- go by, in a canoe - (vta)
gmoodid	- steal - (vai)
gmoodwaad	- stole something from someone - (vta)
gnahmawaad	- warn someone of something - (vta)
gnebigoog	- snakes - (na)
gnomaa	- maybe - (av)
gnoonaan	- spoke to - (vti)
gnoonind	- to talk to - (vta)
gnwezh	- for a long time (av) - refer to noomok
go	- emphatic particle - heightening assertiveness - naa - emphatic particle - marking evaluative info.
gojiing	- outside - (av)
gonda	- these - (an)
gopan	- what he was told - (vta)
goshkoziwaad	- awaken - (vai)
gpagziwag	- thick - (av)

gpiisiiwag	- they don't go inland - (vta)
gshkitoogwenh	- wonder how he did it - (vai)
gshkitoosiin	- could not do this - (vti)
gshkomaan	- startle someone - (vta)
gtimaadzid	- lives a lazy life - (vai)
gwaabiignan	- lift out of the water - (vta)
gwaambdaanaawaa	- you see (pl) - (vta)
gwaashknjigwaashkni	- jump out - (vai)
gwaashkweziwag	- spunky - (vii)
gwiiwzens	- a boy - (na) var. gwiizehns
gyak	- straight - (av)
Gzhe Mnidoo	- Great Spirit, Creator - (na)
gzhihewziwin	- power - (ni)
gzhiikaad	- he was fast - (vta)
gzhiiweszinoon	- ring not as loud - (vai)
iidig	- must be, maybe - (av)
iishpin	- if - (av)
ishpiming	- up, skywards - (av)
iw	- that (pn) - also means i
jekbideg	- plowed into - (vai)
jepziwag	- be athletic - (aj)
ji	- future tense - (pv)
Jibwek	- the Ojibwe - (na)
jiibaakwaad	- (they) cooked for someone - (vta)
jiibaakwaaged	- do the cooking - (vai)
jiibaakwesii	- does not cook - (vta)
jiigbiig	- the waterfront - (ni)
jiigi	- near, by - (pn)

Glossary - Ojibwe to English

jiigyahiing — near something, by something - (av)

jiimaan — canoe, boat - (ni)

jiimaanan — boat, canoe (pl) - (ni)

jiimaanenhs — small canoe - (pl) -(ni)

jiimaanenhswaan — their small canoes - (pl) - (ni)

jiimaanenhswaang — into their small canoes - (pl) - (ni)

jiimaaning — in the canoe - (ni)

jiimaanwaa — their canoe - (vti)

jiingtamwaad — (they) had pow wows - (ni)

ka — you will -future tense - (pv)

ka niibaabsiin — you wouldn't have to have a wake - (vti)

kamwaad — lie in ambush for someone - (vta)

kandood — be on the lookout - (vai)

kandwa — be on the lookout - (vai)

kawaabjig — scouts - (na) - refer to ekawaabjig

kawaabmaad — be on the lookout for someone - (vta)

kida — said - (vai)

kidod — say something - (vai)

kidwag — they said - (vai)

kina — all - (aj) - gegoo - everything - go - all of it

kinoohmaagewinan — teachings - (vai)

kinoohmaagying — to learn (somebody teach us) - (vai)

kinoohmaagzid — to be taught - (vai)

kinoohmaajgaaswaad — taught them - (vai)

kinoohmowaawaad — teach someone (something) - (vta)

kiwenziinh — old man - (na)

ko — used to be, since - (pv)

konaashkowaawaan — chased away someone (plural) - (vta)

konaashkwaad	- chased away someone (singular) - (vta)
kookjiishag	- groundhogs - (na)
kwewag	- women - (na)
M'chigiing	- place, West Bay - (na)
maa	- emphatic particle expressing cooperation
maaba	- this - (av)
maage	- or, maybe - (av)
maajaa	- go away - (vai)
maajaahiing	- going away - (vai)
maajaawaad	- all go away - (vai)
maajaayaan	- someone going away - (vai)
maajii	- start, begin - (pv)
maajiigaazo	- was taken away - (vta)
maajiikgzhowewag	- they left, - (vta)
maajiikoshawe	- left, by rowing (sing.) - (vai)
maajiinaad	- take something (an.) away - (vta)
maajiinaazhkawaad	- send someone away - (vta)
maajiishkaawaad	- (they) to grow (spiritually) - (vai)
maajiiwzhiwed	- take people away - (vai)
maamaajaawag	- left one by one (pl) - (vai)
maamkaadenmoog	- in awe (they) - (vai)
maampii	- here, this place - (av)
maanda	- here, (here it is) this - (in)
maandgonwin	- cover something completely (an.) - (vta)
maawnjiding	- they gathered - (vai)
maawnjidwaad	- (they) gathered - (vai)
manjiidig	- I don't know (when) - (pt)
mchaag	- be big - (vii)

mdewesing	- ring - (vii)
mdwedjiwang	- the sound of running water - (vii)
mdweganaajgaazod	- to hit something, to make a sound - (an.) - (vai)
mdwesdoon	- came to ring - (someone) - (vti)
mdwesing	- rings - (vii)
mdwesjigaade	- rung (by someone) - (vti)
mdwesjigeng	- ringing a bell - (vti)
megwaa	- meanwhile - (av)
megwaakwaa	- in the woods - (vii)
Mekdekonye	- priest (one who wears black clothing) - (na) - g, priests
memkaaj	- not necessarily - (av)
memoonji	- the largest - (av)
meshkdoongejig	- traders - (na)
meshkdoonmaagwaad	- exchange, trade with - (vta)
mewzha	- along time ago - (av)
mii	- it is thus, it is so, then - (av) - go - it is so -(av) - go eta - it is only, there is only- (av)
mii maa	- it is there - (av) - sa - that is so (av)
mii dash	- and then, then - (av) - miish - variation
miigaasjig	- those who fight - (na)
miigwechwi'aawaad	- they thank someone for something - (vta)
miijim	- food - (ni)
miijin	- eat something - (vti)
miikaans	- path (ni)
miikan	- road - (ni)
miikanwaa	- (their) path - (ni)
miinaan	- give something to someone - (vta)

miinaawag	- were given to them (pl)- (vta)
miingowewziwaad	- (gift) given to them - (vta)
miingowewziwnan	- gifts (na)
miinwaa	- also, again - (av)
miish	- and then - (av) refer to mii dash
mji	- evil - (pn)
mji-mshkiki	- bad medicine, poison - (ni)
mkaan	- find - (vta)
mkadeke	- fast (not eat) - (vai) - waad, they who fasted (pl)
mkadekewag	- they fasted - (vai)
mkaksagoon	- keg, barrels - (ni)
mkaksagoonhsing	- small kegs, barrels - (ni)
mkawaad	- found him (plural) - (vta)
mkawaasiiwaan	- didn't find someone (they) - (vta)
mkaziinaawaa	- they didn't find - (vta)
mkazwan	- can not find - (vai)
mkindaaganan	- furs - (na)
mkokmigaag	- a mound - (vii)
mkwendang	- remember (something) - (vti)
mndaadendamowin	- respect - (vti)
mndaadendanaawaa	- respectful of something (pl) - (vti)
mndaadendang	- to respect (something) (vti)
mndaadenmaawaad	- to honor, respect someone - (vta)
mngimnagaag	- be big and round - (vii)
Mnidoo	- Great Spirit, Creator - (na)
mnidoomnensag	- beads (na)
mnidoowendaagozi	- was spirit like - (vta) - d, spirit like - (vta)

mnik	- so much, (enough) - (av)
mnikwe	- drink something - (vai)
mnikwejik	- ones who drink - (vai)
mnikwesiiwag	- not drinking (pl) - (vai)
mnis	- island - (ni)
mno	- good - (pv)
mnowendang	- bless something - (vti)
mookiitaagonaanik	- fighters, (enemy) - (na)
mookiitaagook	- (they will) attack someone - (vta)
mookiitaagwaad	- to attack (pl) - (vta)
mookzhowe	- to row, paddle - (vai) - ng, rowing - waad, they paddle
moonaawan	- they took something off - (vti)
msawendang	- be bold - (vai)
mshkiki	- medicine - (ni)
Mshkikinini	- Medicine man - (na)
mshkodeng	- location, on the prairie, in the clearing - (ni)
mshkodewashk	- sage - (na)
mtashkamig	- on the ground - (av)
mtig	- tree - (na)
mtigamig	- log house (na)
mtigoog	- trees - (na)
mtigoong	- on the tree (s) - (na)
mwendaagziwin	- happy, fun - (vai)
myaginishnaabe	- stranger, other Indian - (na)
mzinshin	- leave an imprint - (vai)
mziwe	- all over - (av)
naa	- emphatic particle marking evaluative info.

naabdak	- used for - (vii)
naabndamwaad	- what they dreamt - (vta)
naabndamwin	- dream - (ni)
naabndang	- what one dreamt - (vta)
naad	- he said to him (sing.) (vai)
naadmaagoziwaad	- seek help - (vti)
naadsabiid	- go -check one's net - (vai)
naadsabiinid	- (someone) checking anothers net - (vai)
naadsabiinwag	- go check their net (pl) - (vai)
naagdooyan	- you follow - (vai)
naakniged	- a certain custom, made rules - (vai)
naamkamig	- underground - (av)
naanaagdawendamoog	- meditated (they) - (vai)
naanaagdawendamowaad	- (they) come to meditate (vai)
naanaagdawendang	- meditate - (vai)
naanaawyihiing	- in the middle (of an area) - (av)
naanan	- five - (nm)
naangodnang	- once in awhile - (av)
naaskowaad	- approach someone - (vta)
nahiing	- from this direction - (ni)
nakaaznaawaa	- use something (pl) - (vai)
nakaazo	- use - (vai)
nakaazsiinaawaa	- not used - (vai)
nakaazwaad	- use (they will) - (vai)
nakaazwaajin	- (what) they used - (vta)
nakiid	- worked - (vta)
nakiimgad	- (it) worked - (vai)
nakmigak	- be news, (an event) - (vii)

Glossary - Ojibwe to English

nakzhowed	- paddle in a certain way - (vai)
nambideg	- went into the distance - (vii)
nametamwaad	- bless something - (vti)
namhaad	- pray - (vai)
namhaamwag	- praying - (vai)
namhaawaad	- (they) prayed - (vta)
namo	- a road going in a certain direction - (vii)
nankii	- work (vai)
	- waad, they work
nankiisii	- did not work - (vii)
nbaawaad	- asleep - (pl) (vai)
nbaaying	- we are sleeping - (vai)
nbiing	- in/on the water - (av)
nbiish	- water - (na)
nbod	- (someone) died - (vai)
nboyaanh	- I die (I am gone) - (vai)
nda	- look (to do something) - (pv)
ndawaab	- to look for someone (pl) - (vta)
ndawaambdaanaawaa	- (they) sought - (vta)
ndawendjgenjin	- hunters - (na)
ndawendmaawaan	- wanted someone to do something - (vta)
ndawenjgeng	- hunting - (vai)
ndawenjgewaad	- they went hunting - (vai)
ndaweshsagoog	- confuse (you) - (vii)
nebaad	- who is sleeping (someone) - (vta)
nendam	- thought - (vai)
Neyaabkong	- place, at the point (na)
ngaashmaawaan	- stopped (plural) - (vai)

ngaashmindwaa	- stopped by someone - (vai)
ngaashziiwag	- didn't stop - (vai)
ngadmowaawaan	- they left behind something - (vti)
ngamwag	- (they) sang - (vai)
ngii	- I was (preverb)
ngoding	- once - (av)
ngodwaaswi	- six - (nm)
ngoji	- off somewhere, away, elsewhere - (av)
ngokaan	- graveyard - (ni)
ngokiiwaad	- bury (pl) - (vai)
Ngwis	- my son - (na)
ni	- (pv) - future tense (ni-giiwen, go home!)
ni'aa	- him/her is called (name) - (na)
ni-giiwed	- when he went home - (vta)
niibna	- a lot, much - (av)
niigaan-nendmowin	- telepathy (ni)
niimidim	- dancing (vai)
niin	- me, myself - (na)
niinaa	- sure, I mean to say - (av)
Niipsing	- place, Nipissing - (na)
niish	- two, (nm) variation niizh
niiwgon	- four days - (av)
niiwin	- four (nm)
niiwodbik	- four nights - (av)
niiwogiizhgak	- the fourth day - (av)
niizhgon	- two days - (av)
niizhgongag	- the second day - (av)
niizhobboon	- two years - (vii)

Glossary - Ojibwe to English

niizhwaaswi — - seven - (nm)

nikeyaa — - direction (that way) - (av) also nikehiing

ninaatigo ziiwaagbmide — - Maple syrup - (na)

ninda — - these - (pn)

niniwag — - men (plural) - (ni)

niniwjig — - to become men - (na)

Nishnaabe — - Indian - (na)
- nhs, little Indian

Nishnaabenhsag — - little Indians - (na)

niw — - those

nji — - from a certain direction, place   (pv)

njibaa — - comes from a certain place - (vai)

njibaad — - where one comes from - (vai)

njibaamgadoon — - (things) came from - (vta)

njibaawag — - they come from (somewhere) - (pl) - (vai)

nmadbi — - sit - (vai)
- yaang, sitting around

Nmamaa — - my mother - (na)

Nmishoomis — - my Grandfather - (na)

nongo — - now, today - (av)

nooj — - various - (av) also nawaj

noojmowin — - healing, a cure - (vta)

nookdaawngaak — - soft sand - (ni)

noomok — - for a long time, awhile - (av) refer to gnwezh

noondaagaazo — - is heard yelling (shouting) - (vai)

noondaanaa — - heard (we) - (vai)

noondmowaad — - heard (they) - (vai)

noondwaad — - hears someone - (vta)

Glossary - Ojibwe to English

noondwaan	- hears someone - (vta)
noongo	- now, today - (av) variation nango
noopming	- inland - (av)
noopnadang	- follow something - (vti)
noozwin	- name - (ni)
nsaakse	- opens - (vii)
nsaaksin	- open - (vti)
nshike	- alone - (av)
nsistasii	- not understand - (vti)
nsistawaasiiwaan	- not understood (them) - (vti)
nsoboongis	- be so many years - (av) - widik, maybe this many years
nsognagak	- be three days - (vii)
nswi	- three - (nm)
ntaa	- is good at - (pv)
nwewesing	- sounds like - (vii)
Nwiidgemaagan	- spouse (my wife) - (na)
nwiijkiwehnsag	- little friends - (na)
oo	- to go and do (something) - (pv)
oodaawaad	- to go and live there - (vai)
oodenaang	- in the village - (vii)
oodenaw	- town (village) - (ni)
oodenwesing	- in the little village - (vii)
oodi	- there, over there - (av) - variation - waya
oosan	- his father - (na)
ooya	- somebody, someone - (na) refer to waya
paanankiin	- go about your business - (vai)
pagdood	- threw (at someone) - (vta)

Glossary - Ojibwe to English

Pahiinsag	- little people, elves - (na)
pane	- always - (av)
pii	- when - (av)"
piichi	- in the process of, to the extent that (pv)
piichi-piichbisod	- to the extent, he flew - (vta)
piitendziinaawaa	- reverence - (don't care) - (vai)
pkidgojinoog	- are hanging over (pl)- (vii)
S'gamok	- place, Sagomok - (ni)
sa	- emphatic particle - (av)
sabiin	- net - (ni)
Semaa	- tobacco - (na)
Shawanoswe	- person, goes south, is walking south - (na)
Sheguiandah	- place - (na)
shi	- and - prefix (av)
Shiibaawnaaning	- place, Killarney - (na)
shkahii	- new thing - (ni) - n, new things (pl)
Shkakmikwe	- Mother Earth - (na)
shkinweg	- young men - (na)
shkode	- fire - (ni)
shkodegamgong	- fire house - (ni)
shkodewaaboo	- fire water (liquor) - (ni)
shkodewaaboong	- in the liquor - (vii)
shkonganing	- reservation - (ni)
shkwaa	- after - (av) - ch, last time
shkweyaang	- behind - (av)

sin	- stone - (ni) - iin, stones, (pl)
siniing	- on the stone - (av)
Siniinmedwe'egin	- sounding stones - (na)
Sinmedwe'ek	- place Bell Rocks - (na)
te	- is there - (vii) - g, be there (also "eteg")
temgad	- is there - (vii)
tesnoo	- isn't there - (vii)
wa	- that one - (prefix)
waa	- you will - future tense
waabang	- dawn (morning) - (vii)
waabanong	- in the east - (av)
waabmaad	- saw (something) - (vta)
waabmaasiig	- did not see (someone) - (vta)
waabmaawaad	- they saw (someone) - (vta)
waabmaawaan	- they see them (pl) - (vta)
waabmigaaswag	- were seen - (they) - (vta)
waabndamwaad	- look for (something for someone) - (vta)
waaboowaan	- blanket (that) - (ni)
Waabshkiiyed	- whiteman (English) - (na)
Waabshkiiyejig	- whitemen (English) - (na)
waakaaganing	- in the hollow - (vii)
waakaaksijganan	- large corrals - (ni)
waankewag	- dig holes (pl) - (vai)
waasa	- far (very distant) (av)"
Waasaaksing	- place, Parry Sound - (na)
waase'aabang	- early morning, daylight - (av)

Glossary - Ojibwe to English

Waaseyaabendamowin	- transitional journey youth to adulthood, to live by, adhere to, vision quest
waawaaj	- even - (av)
wan	- fog - (vii)
waya	- someone - (na) refer to ooya
wdasabiiman	- his net - (na)
wenesh	- what - (ni)
wenjishing	- something good - (av)
wesiinhn	- animals - (na)
wewiib	- hurry, quickly - (av)
wi	- that - prefix (ni)
wigwaamesan	- tents - (ni)
wii	- will, want to do something (prefix) future
wiiba	- early - (aj)
wiidookwaad	- to play with someone (pl) - (vta)
wiidookwaawaan	- (they) played with - (vta)
Wiigwaaskingaa	- Land of Birch Trees (place) (na)
wiiji	- with - (pv)
wiijiindiwaad	- go together (pl) - (vta)
wiijiiwed	- go along, accompany - (vta)
wiikaa	- ever (for a long time) - (av)
wiikwed	- Bay (ni) - ong, inlet - (ni)
wiikweyaak	- in another bay (vii)
wiimbaabkaa	- hollowed out rock - (vii)
wiimbnakzid	- hollow sound - (vii)
wiindmaagaazod	- what he was told - (vai)
wiindmaagewag	- they came to tell - (vta)

wiindmaagoon	- (he/they) told him - (vta)
wiindmaawaad	- what they told him (pl) - (vta)
wiindmawaa	- told (something) - (vta)
wiingashk	- sweetgrass - (ni)
wiisning	- eating (vai)
wiisniwaad	- to eat (pl) - (vai)
Wikwemikong	- place - (ni)
wjepzid	- quick - (vai)
wjiimaaning	- his canoe (na)
wnendang	- forget it -(vti)
wnishing	- be lost - (vai)
wnitooyan	- lose something (I) - (vti)
wzhebwaagan	- his oar - (na)
yaa	- to be there - (vai)
yaa'aawaan	- had - (vai)
yaabtaadibikak	- midnight - (av)
yaad	- is there (be on a certain place) - (vai)
yaag	- be there (in a certain place) - (vai)
yaamwaad	- they have or hold something (event) - (vta)
yaanan	- (he) has - (vii)
yaang	- get something - (vti)
yaanid	- come to him - (vii)
yaasii	- not there - (vii)
yaawaad	- get something (an.) - (vta)
yaawag	- be there (in a certain place) - (vii)
yaazho	- the next (day) - (aj)
zaagewewaad	- come out, appear (vai)
zaagjigshowed	- paddle out, away - (vai)

zaagtoowaad	- they cherished - (vti)
zegigoon	- scared (someone) (vta)
zhaabkozhwed	- paddle through - (vai)
zhaabwiiwaad	- they escaped - (vai)
zhaad	- go, goes - (vai)
zhaajig	- they who come - (pl) - (vai)
zhaashgo	- after - (av)
zhaawag	- go, goes - (pl) - (vai)
zhaawnong	- in the south - (av)
zhaayan	- you go - (vai)
zhangem	- given food (vta)
zhebwaagan	- oar - (ni) - an, oars, (pl) - (ni)
zhebwe	- paddle - (vta)
zhengshing	- one who is laying down - (vai)
zhi	- to (a certain place) - (pv)
zhichgaade	- be made - (vii)
zhichge	- do something - (vai) - ng, - someone doing something - (vta)
zhichgenid	- tell someone to do something - (vta)
zhichgeyan	- you do something - (vai)
zhigo	- by now, pretty soon - (av)
zhiibaabiiyaag	- passageway through - (na)
zhiibaakshowe	- row through a narrow passage - (vai)
zhiibaakshowe'iin	- row through a narrow passage - (vai)
zhiibaakshowewaad	- row through a narrow passage (pl) - (vai)
zhiibaashkayan	- go through there (you) - (vti)
zhiingengdaagziinhwag	- they were kind of mischievous - (vta)

zhiitaa	- get ready - (vai) - waad, got ready
zhingwaakoog	- pine trees - (na)
zhinkaadaanaawaa	- they called it (pl) - (vii)
zhinkaade	- called a certain name - (vii)
zhinkaaswaad	- why they are named - (vai)
zhinkaazo	- to be called a certain name (pl) - (vai)
zhinnooged	- point at something - (vta)
zhishing	- in a certain way, how they were placed - (vai)
zhitood	- make something in a certain way - (vti)
zhitooying	- making something - (vta)
zhiwebak	- (what) happened - (vii)
zhiwebnang	- threw it this way - (vti)
zhiwebzid	- have happened to someone - (vai)
zhngishing	- laid down - (vai)
zhoonyaa	- money - (ni)
ziibi	- river - (ni) - ing, on the river - (av)
ziignan	- pour - (vti) - aawaa, pour(pl)
ziisbaakdoke	- make sugar (maple) - (vai) - waad, make maple sugar (pl)